It's another great book from CGP...

This book is bursting with study notes and practice questions to help you become a master of Chemistry at KS3 (ages 11-14).

It's ideal if you're working at a higher level, which would have been called Levels 5-7 in the old Curriculum.

CGP — still the best! ☺

Our sole aim here at CGP is to produce the highest quality books — carefully written, immaculately presented and dangerously close to being funny.

Then we work our socks off to get them out to you — at the cheapest possible prices.

Published by CGP

From original material by Paddy Gannon.

Editors:
Sarah Pattison, Rachael Rogers, Sean Stayte, Hayley Thompson

Contributors:
Chris Enos, Jim Wilson

ISBN: 978 1 78294 111 8

Clipart from Corel®
Printed by Bell & Bain Ltd, Glasgow.

Based on the classic CGP style created by Richard Parsons.

With thanks to Charlotte Burrows, Chris Elliss, Rachel Kordan,
Glenn Rogers and Karen Wells for the proofreading.
With thanks to Laura Jakubowski for the copyright research.

Contents

The Scientific Process

Scientists <u>work scientifically</u> — it's their job. It means they can <u>plan</u> awesome <u>investigations</u>, get <u>useful results</u> and draw <u>scientific conclusions</u> from them. <u>You</u> need to be able to do all that too. Fear not though, this section will tell you <u>everything you need to know</u>. You'll also be <u>tested</u> on different <u>Working Scientifically</u> topics throughout this book — look out for <u>questions</u> with a WS stamp:

A *Hypothesis* is an *Explanation* of *Something*

1) Scientists <u>observe</u> (look at) things they <u>don't understand</u>.

2) They then come up with an <u>explanation</u> for what they've seen.

3) This explanation is called a <u>hypothesis</u>.

Example:

A scientist is looking at <u>why</u> people have <u>spots</u>.

He notices that everyone with spots <u>picks their nose</u>.

The scientist thinks that the spots might be <u>caused</u> by people picking their nose.

Nose picking = spots?

So the <u>hypothesis</u> is: **"Spots are caused by picking your nose."**

4) Next, scientists need to <u>check</u> whether the <u>hypothesis</u> is <u>RIGHT or NOT</u>.

5) They do this by making a <u>prediction</u> and <u>testing</u> it.

You need to be able to make predictions too.

Example:

A prediction is something like: **"People who pick their nose will have spots."**

6) If tests show that the <u>prediction</u> is <u>right</u>, then there's <u>evidence</u> (signs) that the <u>hypothesis is right</u> too.

7) If tests show that the <u>prediction</u> is <u>wrong</u>, then the <u>hypothesis</u> is probably <u>wrong</u> as well.

Other Scientists Test the Hypothesis

1) It's <u>not enough</u> for <u>one scientist</u> to do tests to see if the hypothesis is right or not.

2) That's why scientists <u>publish</u> their <u>results</u> — so <u>other scientists</u> can find out about the hypothesis and do the <u>tests</u> for themselves. Results are published in <u>peer-reviewed journals</u>.

3) Sometimes other scientists will find <u>more</u> evidence that the <u>hypothesis is right</u>.

4) When this happens, the hypothesis is <u>accepted</u> and goes into <u>books</u> for people to learn. An accepted hypothesis is often called a <u>theory</u>.

A <u>journal</u> is a collection of scientific papers. '<u>Peer-reviewed</u>' means other scientists have checked the results and scientific explanations before the journal is published.

I agree...

New science stuff to learn

5) Sometimes the scientists will find <u>evidence</u> that shows the <u>hypothesis is wrong</u>.

6) When this happens, scientists have to either <u>change</u> the hypothesis or come up with a <u>whole new one</u>.

7) Sometimes <u>new evidence</u> will be found that means an <u>accepted theory</u> needs to <u>change</u>. This is how theories <u>develop</u>.

Investigations

Scientists do investigations to <u>find things out</u>. You need to be able to do investigations too...

Investigations Give Us Evidence

1) Scientists carry out <u>investigations</u> to <u>test</u> their <u>predictions</u> and collect <u>evidence</u> to <u>back up their ideas</u>.
2) <u>You</u> need to be able to <u>plan</u> and <u>carry out investigations</u> to test <u>your predictions</u>.
3) You can do investigations in a <u>lab</u> (laboratory) or <u>somewhere else</u>. For example:

   • A <u>lab</u> is the best place to study most <u>chemical reactions</u>.
   • But if you want to know what kind of <u>rocks</u> there are in an area, you'll need to <u>go outside</u>. This is called <u>fieldwork</u>... although it doesn't always have to be done in a field.

Investigations Have to be Fair Tests

1) Before you start an investigation, you need to <u>plan</u> what you're going to do.
2) You need to <u>make sure</u> the investigation you plan will really <u>test</u> whether your prediction is <u>right</u> or <u>not</u>.
3) To do this, you must make sure it will be a <u>FAIR TEST</u>. This means you must...

ONLY CHANGE ONE THING. EVERYTHING ELSE must be kept the SAME.

4) The thing that you <u>CHANGE</u> is called the <u>INDEPENDENT</u> variable.
5) The things that you <u>keep the SAME</u> are called <u>CONTROL</u> variables.
6) The <u>EFFECT</u> that's <u>MEASURED</u> is called the <u>DEPENDENT</u> variable.

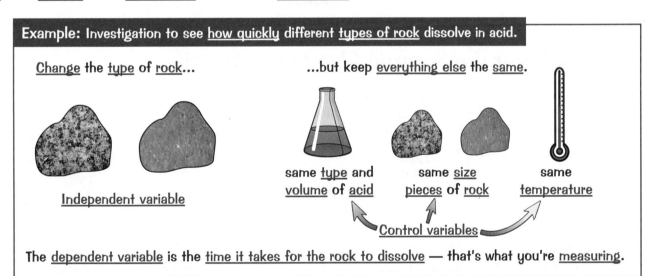

Example: Investigation to see <u>how quickly</u> different <u>types of rock</u> dissolve in acid.

Change the <u>type</u> of <u>rock</u>... Independent variable

...but keep <u>everything else</u> the <u>same</u>. same <u>type</u> and <u>volume</u> of <u>acid</u>, same <u>size</u> pieces of <u>rock</u>, same <u>temperature</u> — Control variables

The <u>dependent variable</u> is the <u>time it takes for the rock to dissolve</u> — that's what you're <u>measuring</u>.

The Equipment Has to be Right for the Job

1) You need to choose the <u>right equipment</u> for your investigation.
2) For example, choose <u>measuring equipment</u> that will let you measure stuff <u>accurately</u>.

If you need to measure out <u>11 ml</u>, this measuring cylinder would be great. It's the <u>right size</u> and you can <u>see</u> where 11 ml is.

This measuring cylinder isn't as good. It's <u>too big</u> and you <u>can't really see</u> where 11 ml is.

Working Scientifically

Investigations Can be Hazardous

1) A <u>hazard</u> is something that <u>could cause harm</u>.

2) Hazards include things like <u>bacteria</u>, <u>chemicals</u>, <u>electricity</u> and <u>fire</u>.

3) Scientists need to <u>manage the risk</u> of hazards by doing things to reduce them.
   For example, if you're using a <u>Bunsen burner</u>:

> • Stand it on a <u>heat-proof mat</u>. This will <u>reduce the risk</u> of starting a <u>fire</u>.
>
> • Always <u>turn it off</u> or to the <u>yellow safety flame</u> when you're <u>not using it</u>.
>   The blue flame is <u>hard to see</u>, so this will reduce the risk of you <u>injuring yourself</u>.

Investigations Need to be Repeated

1) The <u>more times</u> you repeat your investigation the <u>better</u> — but <u>three times</u> is usually enough.
   Then you can work out the <u>mean</u> (average) — see next page.

2) If you get the <u>same</u> or <u>very similar</u> results <u>each time</u> you <u>repeat</u> your
   investigation, that's <u>good news</u>. It means your results are <u>repeatable</u>.

3) It also means that they're <u>more likely</u> to be <u>reproducible</u> by
   <u>other scientists</u>. If other scientists can reproduce your results,
   it's more likely that your <u>hypothesis</u> is <u>right</u> (see p. 2).

4) Results that are both repeatable and reproducible are said to be <u>reliable</u>.

5) Collecting lots of results and calculating a mean can <u>improve accuracy</u>.
   Accurate results are <u>really close</u> to the <u>true answer</u>.

The Bigger the Sample Size the Better

1) Sample size is <u>how many things are in the group you're testing</u>.
   For example, how many <u>rocks</u> you test or how many <u>people</u>.

2) The <u>BIGGER</u> the sample size the <u>BETTER</u> — it means you get <u>more reliable</u> results.

3) But scientists have to be <u>sensible</u> when choosing how big their sample should be.
   If it's <u>too small</u>, their results might not be very accurate.
   If it's <u>too big</u> the investigation might <u>take ages</u> to do.

4) It's best to <u>choose</u> your samples <u>at random</u>. E.g.

> If you're investigating the types of rock found in a field, divide the field into a <u>grid</u> and take
> samples from <u>random squares</u>, <u>all over</u> the field. If you just take samples from one corner,
> you can't be sure that your results represent the types of rock found in the <u>whole</u> field.

Errors Can Pop Up if You're Not Careful

1) The results of your experiment will always <u>vary a bit</u> because of <u>random errors</u>
   — tiny differences caused by things like making a mistake when you're measuring.

2) If the <u>same error</u> is made every time, it's called a <u>systematic error</u>. For example...

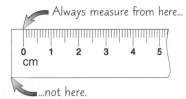

Always measure from here...

...not here.

If you measure from the <u>very end</u> of your <u>ruler</u> instead of from the
<u>0 cm mark</u> every time, <u>all</u> your measurements would be a bit <u>small</u>.

Working Scientifically

Organising and Presenting Data

Once you've collected your data (results) you need to <u>organise</u> and <u>present</u> them <u>nice and clearly</u>.

Data Needs to be Organised

1) Data needs to be <u>organised</u> so it can be processed later on.

2) <u>Tables</u> are dead useful for <u>organising data</u>.

3) You should always make sure that <u>each column</u> has a <u>heading</u> and that you've included the <u>units</u>.

Test tube	Volume of gas produced (cm³)		
	Repeat 1	Repeat 2	Repeat 3
A	28	37	32
B	47	51	60
C	68	72	70

You Might Have to Process Your Data

1) When you've done repeats of an experiment you should always calculate the <u>mean</u> (average).

2) To calculate the mean <u>add together</u> all the data values, then <u>divide</u> by the total number of data values.

Test tube	Volume of gas produced (cm³)				
	Repeat 1	Repeat 2	Repeat 3	Mean	Range
A	28	37	32	(28 + 37 + 32) ÷ 3 = 32.3	37 – 28 = 9
B	47	51	60	(47 + 51 + 60) ÷ 3 = 52.7	60 – 47 = 13
C	68	72	70	(68 + 72 + 70) ÷ 3 = 70.0	72 – 68 = 4

3) You might also need to calculate the <u>range</u> (how spread out the data is).

4) To do this find the <u>largest</u> number and <u>subtract</u> the <u>smallest</u> number from it.

5) You want your results to be as <u>precise</u> (close to the mean) as possible — so the <u>smaller</u> the range, the <u>better</u> your results.

You Can Present Your Data in a Graph or Bar Chart

1) Presenting your data in a graph or bar chart makes it easier to <u>spot patterns</u> in the results (see next page).

2) Whatever type of graph or chart you draw, you must choose a <u>sensible scale</u> for the <u>axes</u> and remember to <u>label</u> them. Make sure you include the <u>units</u> too.

Bar Charts

1) If you're measuring something that comes in <u>categories</u> you should use a <u>bar chart</u> to show the data.

2) <u>Categories</u> are things like 'type of rock'. You <u>can't</u> get results <u>in-between categories</u>.

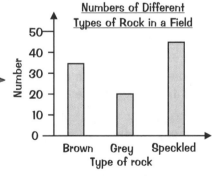

Line Graphs

1) If you're measuring something that can have <u>any value</u> you should use a <u>line graph</u> to show the data.

2) For example, <u>temperature</u>, <u>volume</u> and <u>mass</u> could be shown using a line graph.

3) When you're drawing a line graph, you put the <u>dependent variable</u> (the effect you measure) on the <u>y-axis</u>.

4) The <u>independent variable</u> (the thing you change) goes on the <u>x-axis</u>.

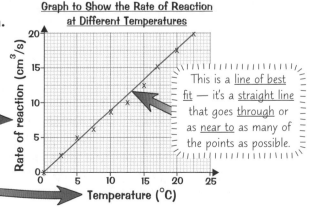

Working Scientifically

Concluding and Evaluating

Drawing a conclusion is all about <u>finding patterns</u> in your data.

Line Graphs Can Show Patterns in Data

1) When you're carrying out an investigation it's not enough to just present your data — you've also got to find any <u>patterns</u> in the data.

2) Line graphs are great for showing patterns in data.

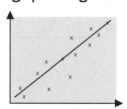

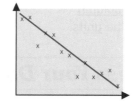

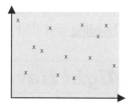

You can see here that as one variable <u>increases</u> the other <u>increases</u> too.

Here, as one variable <u>increases</u> the other <u>decreases</u>.

There's absolutely <u>no</u> <u>pattern</u> to be seen here...

A Conclusion is a Summary of What You've Learnt

1) Once you've organised and presented your data, you need to analyse it and come to a <u>conclusion</u>.

2) You just have to <u>look at your data</u> and <u>say what pattern you see</u>.

<u>EXAMPLE</u>: the table shows how effective two washing powders were at removing stains when used at 30 °C.

Washing powder	% of stained area removed on average
A	60
B	80
No powder	10

<u>CONCLUSION</u>: Powder <u>B</u> is more effective at removing stains than powder A at <u>30 °C</u>.

3) You also need to use the data that's been <u>collected</u> to <u>justify</u> the conclusion (back it up).

> <u>EXAMPLE continued</u>: Powder B removed 20% more of the stained area than powder A on average.

4) You should also use your own <u>scientific knowledge</u> (the stuff you've learnt in class) to try to <u>explain</u> the conclusion.

5) Finally, say whether or not your results <u>back up</u> your original <u>hypothesis</u> — or say whether your original <u>prediction</u> was <u>right or wrong</u>.

Evaluation — Describe How It Could be Improved

In an evaluation you look back over the whole investigation.

1) You should comment on the <u>method</u> — did it produce <u>reliable</u> results? If not, why not? Were there any potential sources of <u>error</u>?

2) Write about the <u>quality</u> of the <u>results</u> too — were they <u>repeatable</u> and <u>accurate</u>?

3) Then you can suggest any <u>changes</u> that would <u>improve</u> the quality of the results. For example, you might suggest changing the way you controlled a variable.

4) Your results might give you ideas for <u>further investigations</u> too. For example, you might come up with a <u>new question</u> that needs answering. Then the whole <u>scientific process</u> starts again...

Heating and Cooling Curves have Flat Bits

Heating and cooling curves show the <u>energy changes</u> that happen when a substance <u>changes state</u>:

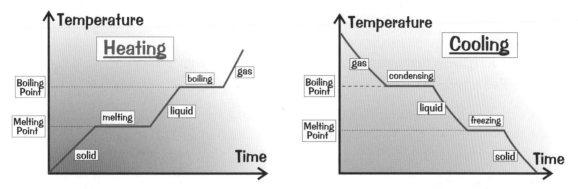

1) The <u>upwards sloping lines</u> on a <u>heating graph</u> show that the <u>temperature</u> is <u>increasing</u>.
2) When a substance is <u>melting</u> or <u>boiling</u>, the lines <u>flatten out</u>. This is because all the <u>heat energy</u> supplied is used to <u>weaken</u> the <u>forces</u> between particles rather than raising the <u>temperature</u>.
3) The <u>downwards sloping lines</u> on a <u>cooling graph</u> show the <u>temperature</u> is <u>decreasing</u>.
4) When a substance is <u>cooled</u>, the cooling graph will show <u>flat bits</u> at the <u>condensing</u> and <u>freezing points</u>.
5) This is because the <u>forces</u> between particles get <u>stronger</u> when a <u>gas condenses</u> or when a <u>liquid freezes</u> — and <u>heat</u> is <u>given out</u>. This means that the temperature <u>doesn't go down</u> until <u>all</u> the substance has <u>changed state</u>.

Fairly Foxy Physical Changes Questions:

Quick Fire Questions

Q1 What happens to the particles of a solid when they are heated?

Q2 What physical change involves a solid turning directly into a gas?

Q3 When a gas is cooled and condensed, what state of matter does it become?

Practice Questions

Q1 An investigation is carried out to find the melting and boiling points of substance X. A pure sample of substance X is **cooled** until it has changed from a **gas** to a **solid**.

(a) The diagram below shows what happens to the particles in the sample as it cools.

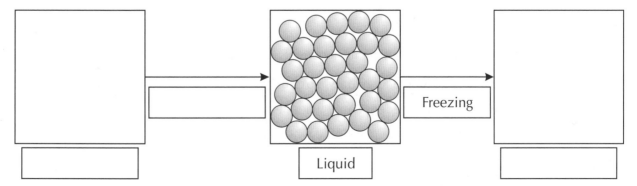

(i) Fill in the missing labels on the diagram.

(ii) In the appropriate boxes on the diagram, draw the arrangement of particles of substance X when it is a gas and when it is a solid.

(b) (i) As substance X cools, how does the movement of its particles change? Explain why.

....

....

(ii) What happens to the **density** of substance X as it becomes a liquid? Explain your answer.

....

....

(c) The diagram opposite shows a simplified cooling graph for substance X.

What letter shows the melting point of substance X?

....

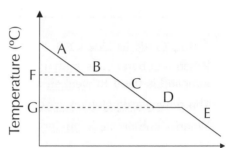

Q2 The diagram on the right shows a simplified heating graph for pure water. At normal atmospheric pressure, pure water boils at 100 °C. Pure ice melts at 0 °C.

(a) What should the label say at G?

....

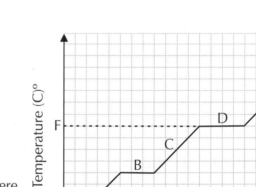

(b) Write down the letters that represent:

(i) ice melting. ....

(ii) water vapour heating up. ....

(c) Write down **two** letters representing stages where bonds between water particles are being broken.

....

(d) What is the temperature at F? .... °C

(e) Which of the following statements is correct? ....

  A The water is gaining energy only at A and C.

  B The water is gaining energy only when its temperature is rising.

  C The water is gaining energy for the whole of the time shown on the graph.

Topic Review | How did you find the questions? Are you happy with the learning objectives?

Section 1 — Classifying Materials

Atoms and Elements

Atoms and elements are the <u>building blocks</u> of <u>everything</u> on the <u>planet</u>. Phew. Better make sure you <u>learn all about them</u> then. After these pages you should:

- know what an <u>atom</u> is — and what <u>Dalton</u> had to say about atoms
- understand the difference between <u>atoms</u> and <u>elements</u>
- know that <u>different elements</u> have <u>different properties</u>
- know that all elements have a <u>name</u> and a <u>symbol</u>.

You Need to Know About Atoms...

1) Atoms are a type of <u>tiny, tiny, particle</u>.

2) They're so small that you <u>can't see them directly</u>. So for a long time, no one knew much about them.

3) <u>Dalton</u> was the first modern scientist to try to <u>explain</u> things about atoms. According to the <u>Dalton model</u>:

- <u>All matter</u> is <u>made up</u> of <u>atoms</u>.
- There are <u>different types of atom</u>.
- Each <u>element</u> (see below) contains a <u>different type</u>.

Scientists now know a lot more about atoms — but luckily, this is all you need to learn for Key Stage 3.

...and Elements

1) An <u>element</u> is a substance that contains <u>only one type</u> of <u>atom</u>.

2) Quite a lot of <u>everyday substances</u> are elements:

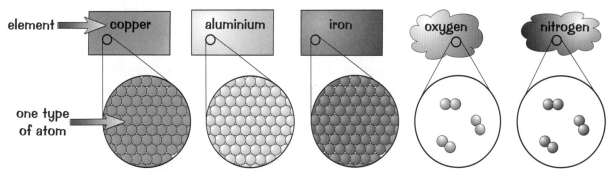

element ⟶ copper   aluminium   iron   oxygen   nitrogen

one type of atom ⟶

3) All of these elements have <u>different properties</u>.
For example, <u>copper</u> is a <u>soft</u>, <u>bendy metal</u>. <u>Oxygen</u> is a <u>colourless gas</u>.

All Elements Have a Name and a Symbol

1) There are over <u>100 different elements</u> and writing their names out each time you wanted to mention one would take ages.

2) So each element has a <u>symbol</u> — usually of <u>one or two letters</u>. The <u>first</u> letter is always a <u>CAPITAL</u>. The <u>second</u> letter is always <u>lower case</u>.

3) You can find the <u>symbol</u> for each element on the <u>periodic table</u> (see page 21). You don't need to learn the symbols for all the elements, but it is worth <u>remembering common ones</u> like these...

Some symbols make sense (like O for oxygen) but others are based on Latin, so are a bit weird — like Fe for iron.

Element	oxygen	carbon	hydrogen	sodium	chlorine	iron	magnesium	aluminium	copper
Symbol	O	C	H	Na	Cl	Fe	Mg	Al	Cu

Amazingly Awesome Atoms (and Elements) Questions:

Quick Fire Question

Q1 Who was Dalton?

Practice Questions

Q1 (a) Which of the following statements about atoms and elements are **true**?
Tick the correct boxes.

☐ All matter is made up of atoms.

☐ There are different types of atom.

☐ Each element is made from two or three types of atom.

☐ Copper atoms are the same as oxygen atoms.

☐ All elements are gases.

(b) Write out a corrected version of every statement you thought was false in part (a).

....

....

....

....

Q2 Draw lines to match up the symbols on the left with the element they stand for on the right.

O   carbon

C   oxygen

Fe   iron

Na   magnesium

Cu   sodium

Mg   copper

Q3 Carbon is an element. If a sample of carbon was broken down into atoms, could the atoms be made into another element? Explain your answer.

....

....

Topic Review Did you feel confident answering the questions? Are you sure you've got all the learning objectives sussed?   ☐   ☐   ☐

Section 1 — Classifying Materials

The Periodic Table

The periodic table is a <u>dead useful way</u> of <u>organising</u> all the elements. By the end of these pages, you should know:

- that <u>elements</u> in the <u>periodic table</u> are arranged into <u>groups</u> and <u>periods</u>
- that elements in the periodic table are also divided into <u>metals</u> and <u>non-metals</u>
- that the elements in a <u>group</u> have <u>similar properties</u>
- how you can use the periodic table to <u>predict patterns in reactions</u>.

The Periodic Table *Lists All the Elements*

1) The periodic table shows all the <u>elements</u> we have <u>discovered</u>.

2) The <u>first version</u> of the table was put together by a scientist called <u>Mendeleev</u>. It's thanks to Mendeleev that <u>elements</u> with <u>very similar properties</u> are arranged into <u>vertical columns</u> in the table.

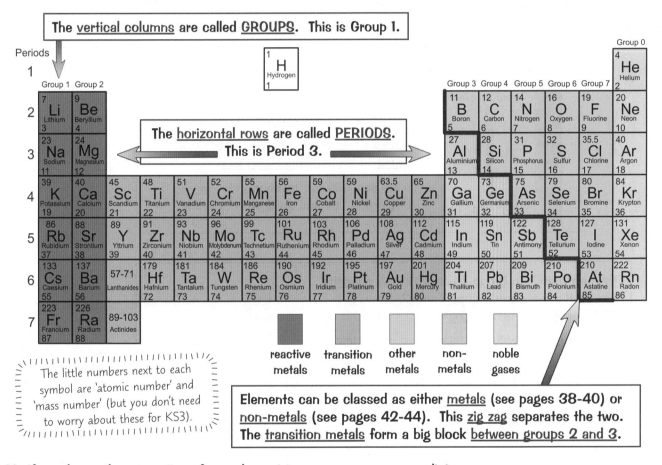

The <u>vertical columns</u> are called <u>GROUPS</u>. This is Group 1.

The <u>horizontal rows</u> are called <u>PERIODS</u>. This is Period 3.

reactive metals | transition metals | other metals | non-metals | noble gases

The little numbers next to each symbol are 'atomic number' and 'mass number' (but you don't need to worry about these for KS3).

Elements can be classed as either <u>metals</u> (see pages 38-40) or <u>non-metals</u> (see pages 42-44). This <u>zig zag</u> separates the two. The <u>transition metals</u> form a big block <u>between groups 2 and 3</u>.

3) If you know the <u>properties</u> of <u>one element</u> in a <u>group</u>, you can <u>predict</u> the properties of <u>other elements</u> in that group. For example:

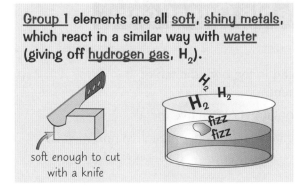

Group 1 elements are all <u>soft</u>, <u>shiny metals</u>, which react in a similar way with <u>water</u> (giving off <u>hydrogen gas</u>, H_2).

soft enough to cut with a knife

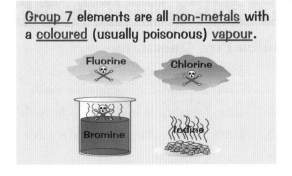

Group 7 elements are all <u>non-metals</u> with a <u>coloured</u> (usually poisonous) <u>vapour</u>.

You Can Use the Periodic Table to Predict Patterns in Reactions

1) In a chemical reaction, <u>elements combine</u> to form new substances (see page 24).
2) An element that's <u>dead keen</u> to combine with other elements is said to be very <u>reactive</u>. <u>Group 1</u>, <u>2</u> and <u>7</u> elements are all <u>pretty reactive</u>.
3) <u>Group 0</u> elements (the "<u>noble gases</u>") are all <u>extremely unreactive</u>. They <u>hardly ever</u> take part in chemical reactions.
4) You can use the periodic table to <u>predict patterns</u> in chemical reactions. For example...

neon

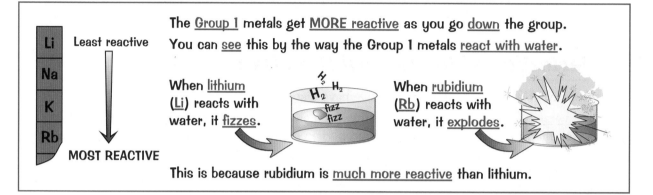

The <u>Group 1</u> metals get <u>MORE reactive</u> as you go <u>down</u> the group. You can <u>see</u> this by the way the Group 1 metals <u>react with water</u>.

When <u>lithium</u> (<u>Li</u>) reacts with water, it <u>fizzes</u>.

When <u>rubidium</u> (<u>Rb</u>) reacts with water, it <u>explodes</u>.

This is because rubidium is <u>much more reactive</u> than lithium.

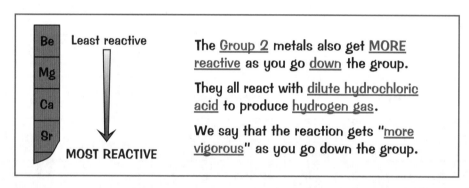

The <u>Group 2</u> metals also get <u>MORE reactive</u> as you go <u>down</u> the group.

They all react with <u>dilute hydrochloric acid</u> to produce <u>hydrogen gas</u>.

We say that the reaction gets "<u>more vigorous</u>" as you go down the group.

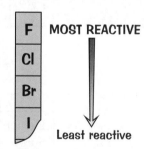

The non-metals in <u>Group 7</u> behave in the <u>opposite</u> way to the metals in Groups 1 and 2. They get <u>LESS reactive</u> as you go <u>down</u> the group.

A <u>more reactive</u> Group 7 element will kick a <u>less reactive</u> Group 7 element <u>out</u> of a <u>salt solution</u>.

E.g. if <u>fluorine</u> (F) is added to a solution of an <u>iodine</u> (I) salt, the fluorine will kick the iodine out of the solution. This is a <u>displacement reaction</u>, see pages 75-76.

Doesn't bother me.

Perfectly Puzzling Periodic Table Questions:

Quick Fire Questions

Q1 How are elements with similar properties arranged in the periodic table? Name the scientist responsible for this arrangement.

Q2 Name two groups in the periodic table which contain very reactive metals.

Q3 Name one group in the periodic table which contains extremely unreactive non-metals.

Practice Questions

Q1 The diagram below shows the symbols of some of the elements and their positions in the periodic table.

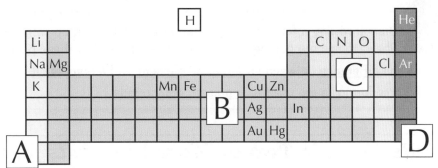

(a) In which of the regions labelled **A** to **D** would you find the following types of element?

(i) The noble gases   **Region** ....

(ii) Non-metals, apart from the noble gases   **Region** ....

(iii) Group 1 elements   **Region** ....

(iv) Group 7 elements   **Region** ....

(b) In which **period** is the element **Ag** (silver)? ....

(c) (i) In which **group** is the element **In** (indium)? ....

(ii) Is **In** a metal or a non-metal? ....

Q2 When a Group 1 metal is cut with a knife, the cut edge starts off shiny, but turns dull as the metal reacts with oxygen.

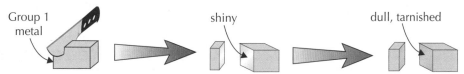

A teacher cuts small blocks of lithium (Li), sodium (Na) and potassium (K) with a knife. Use your scientific knowledge to predict which metal will turn dull the quickest. Explain your answer.

....

....

Q3 The table shows the reactions of some Group 2 metals with water. Use the information in the table and your own knowledge to predict whether **strontium** will react with **cold water**. Explain your answer.

Group 2 metal	Reacts with steam (water vapour above 100 °C)	Reacts with cold water
Beryllium	✗	✗
Magnesium	✔	(✔)*
Calcium	✔	✔
Strontium	?	?

*extremely slowly

....

....

Topic Review How did you find the questions? Are you happy with all the learning objectives?

Section 1 — Classifying Materials

Compounds

Learning Objectives

Start throwing a few <u>elements</u> together and you'll end up with some <u>compounds</u>. Phew, things are getting <u>exciting</u> now. By the end of these pages, you should:

- understand the <u>difference</u> between an <u>atom</u>, an <u>element</u> and a <u>compound</u>
- understand how <u>formulae</u> are used to <u>represent compounds</u>.

Compounds *Contain Two or More* Elements *Joined Up*

1) When <u>two or more atoms</u> join together, a <u>molecule</u> is made. The "<u>join</u>" is known as a <u>chemical bond</u>.

2) <u>Compounds</u> are formed when atoms from <u>different elements</u> join together. Like in CO_2.

"join" or "bond"

3) These diagrams should help you to <u>tell the difference</u> between <u>atoms</u>, <u>elements</u> and <u>compounds</u>:

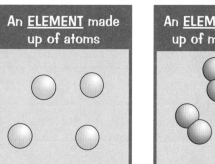

An <u>**ELEMENT**</u> made up of atoms

The atoms are all the same and not joined up — it must be an <u>element</u>.

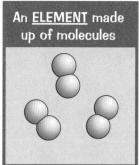

An <u>**ELEMENT**</u> made up of molecules

The atoms are joined, but there's only one type, so it's still an <u>element</u>.

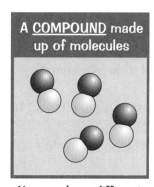

A <u>**COMPOUND**</u> made up of molecules

Here we have different atoms joined together — that's a <u>compound</u> alright.

A <u>**MIXTURE**</u> of different <u>elements</u>

This is <u>not</u> a compound because the elements aren't joined up. It's a <u>mixture</u> (see p. 29).

Compounds *are Formed from Chemical Reactions*

1) In a <u>chemical reaction</u>, chemicals <u>combine together</u> or <u>split apart</u> to form <u>new substances</u>. The chemicals you <u>start with</u> are called <u>reactants</u>. The chemicals you <u>end up with</u> are called <u>products</u>.

2) When a <u>new</u> compound is <u>synthesised</u> (made), elements <u>combine</u>.

3) The <u>new compounds</u> produced by any chemical reaction are always totally <u>different</u> from the <u>original</u> elements (or reactants). The <u>classic example</u> of this is <u>iron</u> reacting with <u>sulfur</u> as shown below:

Iron is <u>magnetic</u>. It reacts with <u>sulfur</u> to make <u>iron sulfide</u>, a totally new substance which is <u>not magnetic</u>.

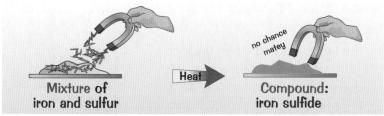

Mixture of iron and sulfur

Heat →

no chance matey

Compound: iron sulfide

4) You can write <u>equations</u> to <u>show what happens</u> in a chemical reaction — see page 58.

Equations are a bit like <u>chemical sums</u>. These equations show what happens when <u>iron</u> reacts with <u>sulfur</u>:

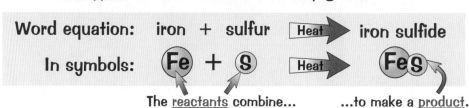

Word equation: iron + sulfur Heat → iron sulfide

In symbols: Fe + S Heat → FeS

The <u>reactants</u> combine...   ...to make a <u>product</u>.

5) Compounds can be <u>split up</u> back into their <u>original</u> elements but it <u>won't</u> just happen by itself — you have to <u>supply</u> a lot of <u>energy</u> to make the reaction go in <u>reverse</u>.

All Compounds Have a Chemical Formula

1) When elements undergo a <u>chemical reaction</u>, the products will always have a <u>chemical formula</u>.

2) The chemical formula for a <u>compound</u> contains the <u>symbols</u> for the <u>elements</u> it's made from.

   > E.g. <u>iron sulfide</u> contains the elements <u>iron</u> (<u>Fe</u>) and <u>sulfur</u> (<u>S</u>). Its <u>formula</u> is <u>FeS</u>.

3) <u>Small numbers</u> in a formula tell you if there's <u>more than one atom</u> present of a particular element.

   > E.g. the formula for <u>water</u> is $\underline{H_2O}$. It contain <u>2 H atoms</u> and <u>1 O atom</u>.

4) This table contains some formulae <u>you'll see a lot</u>. It's worth <u>remembering</u> them — they'll come in dead handy when it comes to writing and understanding <u>symbol equations</u> (see pages 58-59).

   > Formulae is the plural of formula. But you might sometimes see people write 'formulas' — that's okay too.

Compound		Formula
water		H_2O
carbon dioxide		CO_2
hydrochloric acid (stomach acid)		HCl
sulfuric acid (battery acid)		H_2SO_4
sodium chloride (table salt)		NaCl
sodium hydroxide		NaOH

Comically Clever Compound Questions:

Quick Fire Questions

Q1 What is a compound?

Q2 How are compounds formed?

Q3 What is the formula for water?

Q4 What compound does the formula H_2SO_4 represent?

Practice Questions

Q1 Draw lines to match each of the diagrams below with the correct label. You may match more than one diagram to the same label.

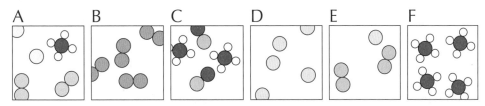

A   B   C   D   E   F

One type of element.

A mixture of compounds.

One type of compound.

A mixture of elements and compounds.

A mixture of elements.

26

Q2 The diagram shows three particles of water.

oxygen atom
hydrogen atom

(a) Why can't water be called an element?

....

....

(b) Why is water called a compound?

....

....

Q3 Which **elements** are in these compounds, and **how many atoms** of each element are there in each compound? Use a periodic table to help you with the symbols.

(a) $FeCl_2$ ....

(d) Fe_2O_3 ....

(b) $ZnCl_2$ ....

(e) $AlCl_3$ ....

(c) HNO_3 ....

(f) $KMnO_4$ ....

Q4 Use the information below to answer the questions that follow.

Sodium is a dull-coloured metal. It is very reactive and must be stored in oil for safety. **Chlorine** is a pale green, toxic gas. Small amounts are used to disinfect swimming pools. A reaction between sodium and chlorine produces a white, crystalline solid, which is commonly known as table salt.

(a) Give **two** pieces of information from the passage that suggest the solid produced is a compound and not a mixture of sodium and chlorine.

1. ....

....

2. ....

....

(b) Explain why it is difficult to get chlorine out of sodium chloride.

....

....

Topic Review How did you get on with the questions? Are you confident on both the learning objectives?

Section 1 — Classifying Materials

Naming Compounds

When it comes to <u>writing chemical equations</u> (see pages 58-59), it's useful to:
* understand how <u>compounds</u> are <u>named</u>.

So that's what you should be able to do by the end of this topic.

Naming Compounds — Two Simple Rules

When elements combine to make a compound, their names change slightly. Learn the <u>Two Simple Rules</u>.

> <u>Rule 1</u>: When <u>two</u> different elements combine the ending is usually "<u>something -ide</u>".

The metal keeps the same name. The non-metal gets the "-ide" on the end.

 NaCl ⟵ Formula ⟶ MgO

Sodium and Chlorine
give: <u>SODIUM CHLORIDE</u> ⟵ Elements present / Name of Compound ⟹ Magnesium and Oxygen
give: <u>MAGNESIUM OXIDE</u>

And in just the
same way:

Sulf<u>ur</u> changes to Sulf<u>ide</u>
Iod<u>ine</u> changes to Iod<u>ide</u>

Brom<u>ine</u> changes to Brom<u>ide</u>
Fluor<u>ine</u> changes to Fluor<u>ide</u>

> <u>Rule 2</u>: When <u>three or more</u> different elements
> combine — and one of them is <u>oxygen</u> —
> the ending will usually be "<u>something -ate</u>".

Again, the name of the metal doesn't change.

 $CuSO_4$ ⟵ Formula ⟶ $CaCO_3$

1 Copper, 1 Sulfur, 4 Oxygens ⟵ Elements present ⟹ 1 Calcium, 1 Carbon, 3 Oxygens
<u>COPPER SULFATE</u> ⟵ Name of Compound ⟹ <u>CALCIUM CARBONATE</u>

And in just
the same
way:

Sodium + Carbon + 3 Oxygens makes: <u>SODIUM CARBONATE</u>
Potassium + Sulfur + 4 Oxygens makes: <u>POTASSIUM SULFATE</u>
Ammonia + Nitrogen + 3 Oxygens makes: <u>AMMONIUM NITRATE</u>

*If Two Identical **Elements** Combine, it's **Not** a Compound*

<u>Identical atoms</u> of the <u>same element</u> are often found <u>combined</u> as <u>molecules</u>.
This <u>doesn't</u> make them a <u>compound</u> though — in fact, their name doesn't even change.

H_2 = Hydrogen (H)(H)
N_2 = Nitrogen (N)(N)
O_2 = Oxygen (O)(O)

F_2 = Fluorine (F)(F)
Cl_2 = Chlorine (Cl)(Cl)
Br_2 = Bromine (Br)(Br)

> These are all <u>elements</u> with <u>two atoms</u>, not compounds. They're almost never found as single atoms in nature.

It's worth <u>learning</u> which elements are usually found combined like this for when you come to
write <u>chemical equations</u>. For example, <u>oxygen</u> in the <u>air</u> around you is <u>oxygen gas</u>, O_2.
So in reactions like <u>combustion</u> (burning in oxygen, see p. 52), oxygen will always take part as O_2.

Naughty but Nice Naming Compounds Questions:

Quick Fire Questions

Q1 Complete the rule for naming compounds:
"When two different elements combine, the ending is usually something ...."

Q2 Give three examples of elements in which the atoms are usually found in pairs.

Practice Questions

Q1 Three substances are shown below.
The diagrams include the chemical symbols of the elements in each substance.

A   **B**   **C**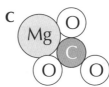

(a) Use the diagrams to complete the table below. You may use a periodic table to help you.

Substance	Name	Chemical formula
A		
B		
C		

(b) Complete these word equations by putting the name of an element or compound in each box.

(i) potassium + chlorine ⟶ [ ]

(ii) sodium + oxygen + carbon ⟶ [ ]

(iii) copper + [ ] + [ ] ⟶ copper sulfate

Challenge Yourself

Q2 Whenever a substance burns or corrodes, it is reacting with **oxygen** in the air.
Everyday names are often used for the substances involved in these common reactions.

For each of the following examples of burning and corrosion, write down
the chemical name of the substance highlighted in bold.

(a) **Rust** is the name given to corroded iron. ....

(b) Carbon dioxide is produced when **charcoal** is used as cooking fuel on barbecues.

....

Topic Review How did you get on with the questions?
Have you nailed the learning objective?

Section 1 — Classifying Materials

Mixtures

Stand by for a big surprise — the substances in a mixture are <u>mixed together</u>. Mind blowing, I know. By the end of these pages, you should...

- know what a <u>pure substance</u> is
- know what a <u>mixture</u> is
- know how mixtures can be made by <u>dissolving</u>.

Mixtures are Substances That are NOT Chemically Joined Up

1) A <u>pure substance</u> is made up of only <u>one type</u> of <u>element</u> (see p. 19) OR only <u>one type</u> of <u>compound</u> (see p. 24). It <u>can't</u> be <u>separated</u> into anything simpler without a <u>chemical reaction</u>.

   E.g. <u>pure water</u> is made up of H_2O <u>molecules only</u>. These molecules can't be separated into H and O atoms <u>without</u> a chemical reaction.

2) A <u>mixture</u> contains <u>two</u> or more <u>different substances</u>. These substances aren't chemically joined up — so, if you're clever, you can <u>separate</u> them very <u>easily</u> using <u>physical methods</u> (i.e. without a chemical reaction). See pages 32-34 for more.

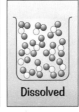

N_2 O_2 CO_2

Air is a mixture of different gases

3) <u>Sea water</u> and <u>air</u> are good <u>examples</u> of mixtures — they contain several different substances which aren't chemically combined.

4) A mixture has the <u>properties</u> of <u>its constituent parts</u> (i.e. the parts it's made from).

Dissolving isn't Disappearing

1) <u>Dissolving</u> is a common way mixtures are made.

2) When you add a solid (the <u>solute</u>) to a liquid (the <u>solvent</u>) the <u>bonds</u> holding the solute particles together sometimes <u>break</u>.

3) The solute particles then <u>mix</u> with the particles in the liquid forming a <u>solution</u>.

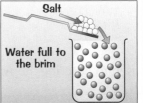

Salt — Water full to the brim

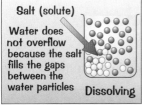

Salt (solute) — Water does not overflow because the salt fills the gaps between the water particles — Dissolving — Dissolved

<u>Learn</u> these seven definitions:

1) <u>Solute</u> – is the solid being dissolved.
2) <u>Solvent</u> – is the liquid it's dissolving into.
3) <u>Solution</u> – is a mixture of a solute and a solvent that does not separate out.
4) <u>Soluble</u> – means it <u>WILL</u> dissolve.
5) <u>Insoluble</u> – means it will <u>NOT</u> dissolve.
6) <u>Saturated</u> – a solution that won't dissolve any more solute at that temperature.
7) <u>Solubility</u> – a measure of how much solute will dissolve.

4) Remember, when salt <u>dissolves</u> it hasn't <u>vanished</u> — it's still <u>there</u> — <u>no mass</u> is lost.

5) If you <u>evaporated</u> off the <u>solvent</u> (the water), you'd see the <u>solute</u> (the salt) again.

20g Salt   Added to 100g Water = 120g Solution

Solubility Increases with Temperature

1) At <u>higher</u> temperatures <u>more solute</u> will dissolve in the <u>solvent</u> because particles move faster.

2) However <u>some</u> solutes won't dissolve in certain <u>solvents</u>. E.g. salt won't dissolve in petrol.

Mind-Bendingly Magnificent Mixtures Questions:

Quick Fire Questions

Q1 What is a pure substance? Give an example.

Q2 Which is generally easier to separate into simpler components — a mixture or a pure substance?

Q3 What is solubility a measure of?

Q4 Explain what the terms soluble and insoluble mean.

Practice Questions

Q1 Many common substances are mixtures.

(a) Underline **three** examples of mixtures in the list below.

      sea water   **oxygen**   **air**   **ink**   **sodium chloride**   **ice**   **nitrogen**   **steam**

(b) Are the particles in a mixture all the same? Explain your answer.

....

....

Q2 Amma added 10 g of salt to 100 g of water. It dissolved completely.

(a) What was the mass of the salt solution?

.... g

(b) What term could be used to describe the **water** in the solution?

....

(c) What term could be used to describe the **salt** in the solution?

....

(d) Describe what happens to the salt particles when the salt dissolves in the water.

....

....

....

....

(e) Amma does the experiment again, this time adding salt until no more will dissolve.
Which term could be used to describe Amma's new solution?

....

Challenge Yourself

Q3 The graph below shows how temperature affects the maximum
mass of potassium iodide that will dissolve in 100 cm³ of water.

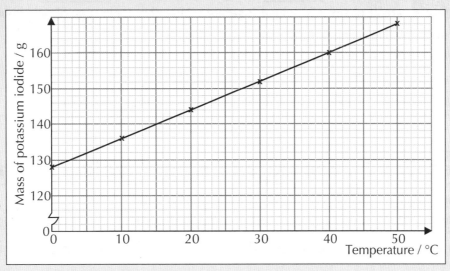

(a) Describe how changing the temperature affects the amount
of potassium iodide that will dissolve in water.

....

....

(b) What mass of potassium iodide will dissolve in 100 cm³ of water at:

(i) 15 °C? ....   (ii) 35 °C? ....

(c) A saturated solution of potassium iodide in 100 cm³ water at 40 °C is made up.
It then cools to 25 °C. Some of the potassium iodide crystallises out of the solution as it cools.

Fill in the labels on the diagram below to show the mass of the **solution** before and
after cooling, and the mass of **potassium iodide** that crystallises out of the solution.
Use the graph above to help you. Note that 1 cm³ of water has a mass of 1 g.

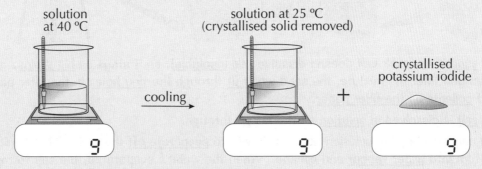

You can do any working out in the space below:

Topic
Review

How did you get on with the questions?
Are you confident on all the learning objectives?

Section 1 — Classifying Materials

Separating Mixtures

Mixtures are <u>dead easy</u> to separate because the <u>substances</u> they're made up of <u>aren't chemically joined</u> together. After this topic, you should know how to...

- separate a mixture using <u>filtration</u> and <u>evaporation</u>
- separate a mixture using <u>chromatography</u>
- separate a mixture using simple or fractional <u>distillation</u>
- <u>check</u> the <u>purity</u> of a <u>substance</u> or <u>identify it</u> using <u>melting</u> and <u>boiling</u> points.

Mixtures *Can be Separated Using Physical Methods*

There are <u>four separation techniques</u> you need to be familiar with.

1) <u>FILTRATION</u>   2) <u>EVAPORATION</u>   3) <u>CHROMATOGRAPHY</u>   4) <u>DISTILLATION</u>

All four make use of the <u>different properties</u> of the <u>constituent parts</u> to <u>separate</u> them out.

Filtration *and* Evaporation — *E.g. for the* Separation *of Rock Salt*

1) <u>Rock Salt</u> is simply a <u>mixture</u> of <u>salt</u> and <u>sand</u> (they spread it on the roads in winter).

2) Salt and sand are both <u>compounds</u> — but <u>salt dissolves</u> in water and <u>sand doesn't</u>. This <u>vital difference</u> in their <u>physical properties</u> gives us a great way to <u>separate</u> them.

You Need to Learn the Four Steps of the Method:

1) <u>Grinding</u>   2) <u>Dissolving</u>   3) <u>Filtering</u>   4) <u>Evaporating</u>

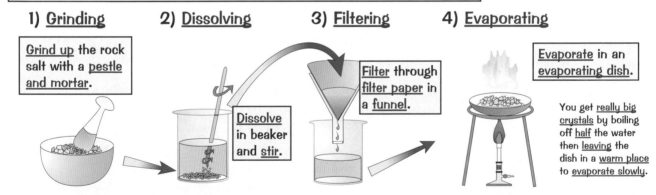

<u>Grind up</u> the rock salt with a <u>pestle and mortar</u>.

<u>Dissolve</u> in beaker and <u>stir</u>.

<u>Filter</u> through filter paper in a <u>funnel</u>.

<u>Evaporate</u> in an evaporating dish.

You get <u>really big crystals</u> by boiling off <u>half</u> the water then <u>leaving</u> the dish in a <u>warm place</u> to <u>evaporate slowly</u>.

- The <u>sand</u> in the rock salt doesn't dissolve (it's <u>insoluble</u>), so it stays as <u>big grains</u>. When you filter the mixture, the sand <u>won't fit</u> through the <u>tiny holes</u> in the filter paper — so it <u>collects on the filter paper</u>.
- The <u>salt</u> is dissolved in <u>solution</u> so it does go through.
- You can then <u>boil</u> the solution you're left with to <u>evaporate off</u> the water. The liquid water will turn into <u>water vapour</u> and escape. When the water's evaporated, the salt forms as <u>crystals</u> in the <u>evaporating dish</u>. This is called <u>crystallisation</u>. (Surprise surprise.)

Chromatography *is Ideal for Separating* Dyes *in Inks*

1) <u>Ink</u> is a <u>mixture</u> of several different <u>dyes</u>.

2) Chromatography uses a <u>solvent</u> soaking through <u>chromatography paper</u> to separate the dyes.

3) <u>Different dyes</u> will <u>travel along</u> the paper at <u>different speeds</u> (see next page).

4) Some will <u>stick</u> to the <u>paper</u> and others will <u>dissolve</u> in the <u>solvent</u> and <u>travel</u> through it <u>quickly</u>.

There are *Two Different Methods* of *Chromatography*

Method 1

1) Put a <u>dot of ink</u> in the middle of a circular piece of <u>chromatography paper</u> (you could also use <u>filter paper</u>).

2) Cut a <u>wick</u> from part of the paper (as shown).

3) Stick the chromatography paper on top of a <u>beaker of solvent</u> (e.g. water) so that the wick's dipping <u>into</u> the solvent.

4) The <u>solvent</u> seeps up the wick and washes the <u>dyes</u> in the ink towards the edges of the paper.

5) The dyes <u>travel outwards</u> at <u>different speeds</u>. So each dye will form a <u>ring</u> in a different place.

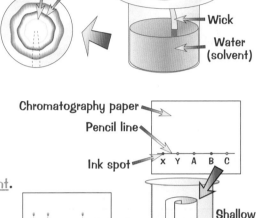

Method 2

1) Draw a <u>pencil</u> line near the bottom of some <u>chromatography paper</u>.

2) Put <u>spots</u> of <u>inks</u> along the line.

3) <u>Roll</u> the paper up and put it in a <u>beaker</u> of <u>shallow solvent</u>.

4) The solvent <u>seeps</u> up the paper. The ink <u>dyes</u> are <u>carried</u> with it.

5) The dyes <u>travel up</u> the paper at <u>different speeds</u>. So each dye will form a <u>spot</u> in a different place.

You Can Analyse Substances Using Chromatography

Chromatography isn't just a great way of <u>separating dyes</u>, oh no. A <u>chromatogram</u> — that's the <u>pattern</u> of spots or rings left behind — can tell you loads of <u>information</u> about inks and other mixtures.

The More Soluble a Dye is, The Further it Travels

1) How <u>far</u> a dye travels depends on how <u>soluble</u> it is in the solvent.

2) Dyes that are <u>really soluble</u> get dissolved in the solvent and <u>transported</u> a long way.

3) If a dye is <u>insoluble</u> it <u>won't move</u> at all.

Comparing Inks Using Chromatography

1) Ink is a <u>mixture</u> of dyes. The <u>same dye</u> will always travel the <u>same distance</u> up the paper. So if two spots are at the <u>same height</u>, they must be the <u>same substance</u>.

2) A particular ink will <u>always</u> leave a characteristic <u>pattern of spots</u> on a chromatogram.

3) For example, if you wanted to find out who <u>forged a signature</u>, you could <u>compare</u> the ink from the <u>forgery</u> with the ink from some <u>suspects' pens</u>.

4) The <u>culprit's ink</u> will have exactly the same <u>pattern of spots</u> as the ink from the forgery.

Chromatography can also be used to investigate <u>blood samples</u> and <u>chlorophyll</u>.

Suspect B is most likely to be guilty, because the ink from their pen contains exactly the same dyes as the pen that wrote the forgery.

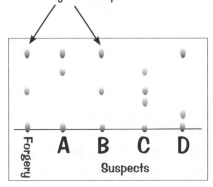

Simple Distillation Separates Pure Water from Ink

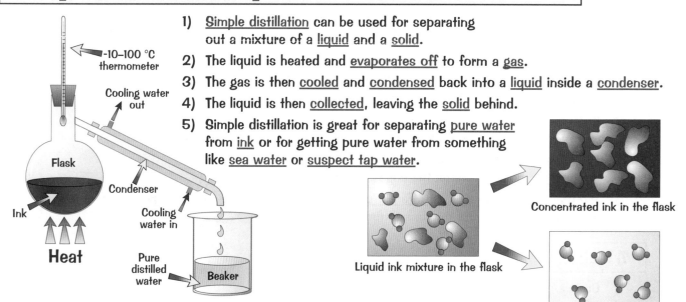

1) <u>Simple distillation</u> can be used for separating out a mixture of a <u>liquid</u> and a <u>solid</u>.

2) The liquid is heated and <u>evaporates off</u> to form a <u>gas</u>.

3) The gas is then <u>cooled</u> and <u>condensed</u> back into a <u>liquid</u> inside a <u>condenser</u>.

4) The liquid is then <u>collected</u>, leaving the <u>solid</u> behind.

5) Simple distillation is great for separating <u>pure water</u> from <u>ink</u> or for getting pure water from something like <u>sea water</u> or <u>suspect tap water</u>.

Concentrated ink in the flask

Liquid ink mixture in the flask

Pure water in the beaker

Fractional Distillation Separates Mixed Liquids

1) <u>Fractional distillation</u> is used for separating a mixture of liquids like <u>crude oil</u>.

2) <u>Different liquids</u> will evaporate off at <u>different temperatures</u>, around their <u>own boiling point</u>.

3) The <u>fractionating column</u> ensures that the "wrong" liquids <u>condense</u> back <u>down</u>, and only the liquid properly <u>boiling</u> at the temperature on the thermometer will make it to the top.

4) When each liquid has <u>boiled off</u>, the temperature reading <u>rises</u> until the <u>next</u> fraction starts to boil off.

5) Real life <u>examples</u> include:
   - distilling <u>whisky</u>,
   - separating <u>crude oil</u> into petrol, diesel and other fuels.

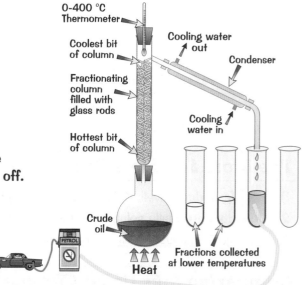

Check Purity with Melting and Boiling Points

1) A <u>pure</u> chemical substance has <u>fixed melting and boiling points</u>. E.g. pure water boils at 100 °C and pure ice melts at 0 °C. These figures are <u>known</u> for a huge range of substances.

2) This helps us to <u>identify unknown</u> substances, e.g. if a liquid boils at <u>exactly</u> 100 °C it's likely to be <u>pure</u> water.

3) <u>Impurities change</u> melting and boiling points, e.g. impurities in water cause it to boil <u>above</u> 100 °C.

4) This means you can <u>test the purity</u> of a substance you've separated from a mixture by <u>boiling</u> or <u>melting</u> it.

Pure Substance	Melting Point °C	Boiling Point °C
Water	0	100
Ethanol	-114	78
Aluminium	660	2520

Simply Stunning Separating Mixtures Questions:

Quick Fire Questions

Q1 When the water in a salt solution evaporates, salt crystals form. What is this process called?

Q2 Which piece of equipment is **not** needed for carrying out simple distillation
— a fractionating column, a thermometer or a condenser?

Q3 What temperature does pure water boil at? What temperature does pure ice melt at?

Practice Questions

Q1 These sentences describe how a solution can be separated into a liquid and a solid using simple distillation. Put the sentences in order by writing the numbers 1-7 in the boxes. The first one has been done for you.

The gas turns
back into a liquid.

The pure liquid
is collected.

The solution is
heated up. 1

The liquid
begins to boil.

The gas travels to
the cool condenser.

The condenser
cools the gas.

The liquid turns
into a gas.

Q2 Blue ink is a mixture of coloured dyes and water. It can be separated into the dyes and water using this apparatus.

wet paper towel · delivery tube · conical flask · blue ink · heat · colourless liquid (water)

(a) Why is the ink heated?

....

(b) Suggest what the wet paper towel and the delivery tube are there to do.

....

....

(c) Why is the water colourless and not blue?

....

(d) How could you check that the liquid was really pure water?

....

....

Q3 Jen drops a glass bottle full of sugar cubes. It smashes, mixing tiny bits of broken glass into the sugar. She uses the procedure shown below to get the sugar back.

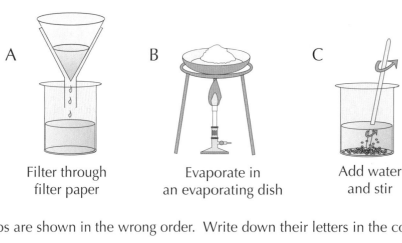

A
Filter through
filter paper

B
Evaporate in
an evaporating dish

C
Add water
and stir

(a) The steps are shown in the wrong order. Write down their letters in the correct order.

1 .... 2 .... 3 ....

(b) (i) Which step separates the glass from the sugar? ....

(ii) Which step involves crystallisation? ....

(c) Suggest **one** safety precaution Jen should take during this procedure. (WS)
Explain your answer.

....

....

Q4 Asif reads that the colour green is a mixture of blue and yellow. He decides to check that this is true using the ink in his green felt-tip pen. His experiment is shown opposite.

green
ink spot

wick

water

(a) Explain how the water from the beaker separates the inks.

....

....

....

....

(b) Asif's teacher tells him that yellow dye is more soluble in water than blue dye. On the filter paper to the right, draw and label what Asif would see at the end of the experiment.

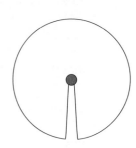

Q5 Jamie separates a mixture of alcohol (boiling point 78 °C) and water using the apparatus shown.

(a) What separation technique is Jamie using?

....

(b) In the diagram, what liquid is being collected in the test tube? Explain your answer.

....

....

....

....

Thermometer reading 78 °C

Cold water out

Condenser

Column filled with glass rods

Cold water in

Flask

Alcohol and water mixture

Heat

(c) The graph below shows what happens to the thermometer reading during the experiment.

(i) Will the water be collected during stage A, B, C or D?

....

(ii) During which stage will Jamie have to change the collecting test tube — A, B, C or D? Explain your answer.

....

....

....

Q6 A sweet was tested to find out which food dyes it contained. It was compared to four other sweets — A, B, C and D. The results are shown below.

(a) Which separation method was used to test the sweets?

....

(b) Which sweet the is the same as the sample sweet? Explain your answer.

....

....

Sample   A   B   C   D

Topic Review What did you think of all those questions? Do you reckon you've got those learning objectives sorted?

Section 1 — Classifying Materials

Properties of Metals

Metals are used for loads of stuff. That's because they have so many useful properties. At the end of this topic, you should...
- be able to describe and explain some of the different properties of metals.

1) Metals Can be Found in the Periodic Table

1) Most of the elements in the periodic table are metals.
2) Some are shown here in red, to the left of the zig zag.

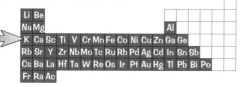

2) Metals Conduct Electricity

1) Electric current is the flow of electrical charge around a circuit.
2) Metals conduct electricity, which means they allow electrical charge to pass through them easily.
3) The moving charges are negatively-charged particles called electrons.
4) Metals contain some electrons that are free to move between the metal atoms. These free electrons can carry an electric current from one end of the metal to the other.
5) Because they conduct electricity well, metals are often used to make wires and parts of electrical circuits. Copper is a good example of a metal used in this way.

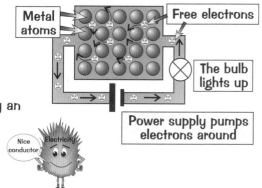

Metal atoms

Free electrons

The bulb lights up

Power supply pumps electrons around

Nice conductor

Electricity

3) Metals Conduct Heat

1) This means metals let thermal energy pass through.
2) The "hot" particles vibrate strongly.
3) Because the particles are very close together, the vibrations are easily passed on through the metal.
4) Free electrons in the metal also help to transfer heat energy from the hot parts of the metal to the cooler parts as they move around.
5) This is why you get things like saucepans made out of metal, e.g. aluminium. Heat from the hob passes easily through the pan and cooks your spaghetti.

CONDUCTION OF HEAT

HOT

HEAT FLOW

COLD

Lots of movement   Little movement

4) Metals are Strong and Tough

1) Metals have high tensile strength (they can be pulled hard without breaking).
2) This is because there are strong forces between metal atoms that hold them together.
3) So they make good building materials. Bridges are often made out of metals like iron or steel.

5) Metals are Shiny When Polished

Polished or freshly cut metals give strong reflection of light from their smooth surface. This makes them look shiny.

6) Metals are Malleable

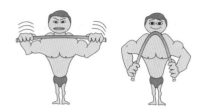

1) Metals are easily shaped (malleable) because the atoms in metals can slide over each other.

2) This means metals can be hammered into thin sheets or bent — all without shattering.

3) This is dead useful. For example...

Thin sheets of aluminium foil can be made by passing bars of aluminium between heavy rollers.

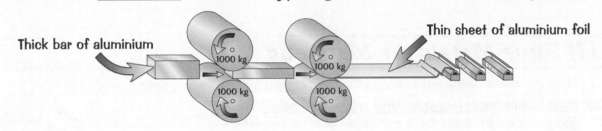

Thick bar of aluminium

Thin sheet of aluminium foil

7) Metals are Ductile

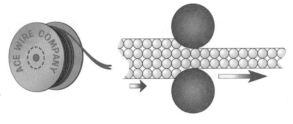

1) This means they can be drawn into wires — like copper in electrical wires (see previous page).

2) Metals aren't brittle like non-metals (pages 42-44) are. They just bend and stretch.

8) Metals have High Melting and Boiling Points

1) A lot of heat energy is needed to melt metals.

2) This is because their atoms are joined by strong forces. So you need to put loads of energy in to weaken the forces.

3) The table shows how hot they have to get to melt.

Metal	Melting Point (°C)	Boiling Point (°C)
Aluminium	660	2520
Copper	1085	2562
Magnesium	650	1090
Iron	1538	2861
Zinc	420	907
Silver	962	2162

9) Metals have High Densities

1) Density is all to do with how much stuff there is squeezed into a certain space.

2) Metals feel heavy for their size (i.e. they're very dense) because they have a lot of atoms tightly packed into a small volume.

3) Most metals are denser than most non-metals.

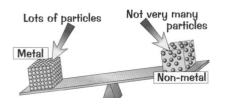

Lots of particles

Not very many particles

Metal

Non-metal

Substance		Density (g / cm³)
non-metals	sulfur	2.1
	carbon	2.3
	iodine	6.2
metals	iron	7.9
	lead	11.3
	gold	19.3

Section 1 — Classifying Materials

10) Metals Make Alloys When Mixed with Other Metals

1) A <u>combination</u> of different metals is called an <u>alloy</u>.
The <u>properties</u> of the metals get <u>jumbled up</u> in the new <u>alloy</u>.

2) So, for example, <u>lighter, weaker metals</u> can be <u>mixed</u> with <u>heavier, stronger metals</u> and the <u>result</u> is an <u>alloy</u> which is <u>light and strong</u>.

Alloy Wheels — light and strong

<u>Stainless steel</u> is used to make <u>knives and forks</u> because it's <u>strong</u> and <u>doesn't rust</u>.

Iron is strong, but it rusts when it gets wet. **+** Chromium metal doesn't rust. **+** Small amount of carbon **=** Stainless steel

11) Some Metals are Magnetic

1) Magnetic means <u>attracted</u> to magnets. Only <u>certain metals</u> are magnetic.

2) <u>Most</u> metals <u>aren't magnetic</u>. <u>Iron</u>, <u>nickel</u> and <u>cobalt</u> are. <u>Alloys</u> made with these three metals will also be magnetic — e.g. <u>steel</u> is made mostly from <u>iron</u>, so is also <u>magnetic</u>.

Iron or nickel or cobalt (or an alloy containing one of them)

12) Metals are Sonorous

This means they make a nice "<u>donnnnggg</u>" sound when they're hit. If you think about it, it's <u>only metals</u> that do that — you <u>could</u> make a gong out of plastic, but it wouldn't be much good.

Gong
Gong

Possibly Puzzling Properties of Metals Questions:

Quick Fire Questions

Q1 Metals let electrons pass through them easily. What are electrons?

Q2 What kind of surface do polished metals have?

Q3 Which property of metals makes them good for making gongs?

Q4 What does it mean if a metal is ductile?

Practice Questions

Q1 Mumetal® is a mixture of iron, nickel and molybdenum.
It is used in thermal imaging cameras and certain types of microscope.

(a) What name is given to a mixture of metals? Circle the correct answer.

magnet   insulator   electron   conductor

atom   alloy   wire

(b) Would you expect Mumetal® to be magnetic? Explain your answer.

....

....

Q2 Read the following statements about metals.

A   All metals are magnetic.

B   Metals are shiny when polished

C   Metals can be drawn into wires.

D   Metals are brittle.

E   Metals are electrical insulators, meaning they allow electrical charges to pass through them.

F   The left-hand side of the Periodic Table lists metals.

(a) Which **three** statements are correct? ....

(b) Use the space below to rewrite the other statements so that they are correct.

Letter .... Statement ....

....

Letter .... Statement ....

....

Letter .... Statement ....

....

Q3 Explain the following properties of metals in terms of their atoms.

(a) Malleable

....

....

(b) High density

....

....

(c) Good conductors of heat

....

....

Topic Review Did you feel confident answering the questions?
Do you know the learning objective inside out?

Section 1 — Classifying Materials

Properties of Non-metals

Learning Objective

The properties of non-metals <u>vary</u> massively. They are very different to metals, but they still do have some <u>useful</u> properties. After this topic, you should...

- be able to describe and explain some of the different <u>properties</u> of <u>non-metals</u>.

1) Non-metals *Can be Found in the Periodic Table*

1) All the non-metals (with the exception of hydrogen) are clustered in the corner over on the <u>right</u> of the <u>zig zag</u>. Look, right over there.

2) There are <u>fewer</u> non-metals than metals.

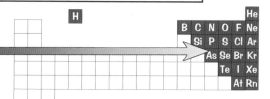

2) Non-metals *are Poor Conductors* of Electricity

1) Most non-metals are <u>electrical insulators</u>, which means that they <u>don't conduct electricity</u>.

2) The atoms in non-metals are <u>arranged</u> so that <u>electrons</u> (negative charges) <u>can't move</u> through them.

3) If electrons can't move then <u>no electric current flows</u>.

4) This is <u>very useful</u> — non-metals combine to make things like <u>plugs</u> and electric cable <u>coverings</u>.

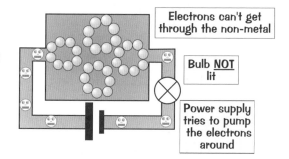

Electrons can't get through the non-metal

Bulb **NOT** lit

Power supply tries to pump the electrons around

GRAPHITE

1) One exception to this rule is <u>graphite</u> — a <u>non-metal</u> made from <u>carbon atoms</u>.

2) Its atoms are arranged in <u>layers</u>.

3) <u>Electrons</u> can move <u>along</u> the layers, allowing graphite to <u>conduct</u> electricity.

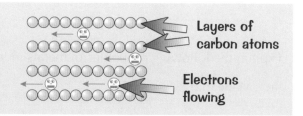

Layers of carbon atoms

Electrons flowing

3) Non-metals *are Poor Conductors* of Heat

1) <u>Heat</u> does <u>not</u> travel very well at all through non-metals.

2) "<u>Hot</u>" particles <u>don't</u> pass on their <u>vibrations</u> so well.

3) This makes non-metals really good <u>thermal insulators</u> (<u>insulators</u> of <u>heat</u>).

4) That's why non-metals are used to make things like saucepan handles.

Saucepan Handles

1) Metal saucepans get <u>very hot</u> during cooking, so the handles are often made of <u>plastic</u>.

2) Plastic is made of <u>non-metal</u> elements, which <u>don't conduct heat</u>.

3) This means you can pick up the pan by its handle, <u>without</u> getting <u>burned</u>.

4) Non-metals are NOT Strong or Hard-Wearing

1) The forces between the particles in non-metals are weak — this means they break easily.
2) It's also easy to scrub atoms or molecules off them — so they wear away quickly.

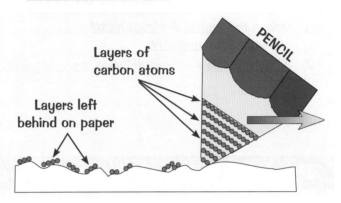

This carbon brush keeps wearing out

WRITING WITH A PENCIL

1) The "lead" in pencils is actually our old friend graphite (see previous page).
2) The layers of carbon atoms are held together by weak forces.
3) When you write with a pencil, tiny bumps in the paper scrub off layers of carbon atoms.
4) Pencils have to be sharpened because the tip is always wearing away.

Layers of carbon atoms

Layers left behind on paper

PENCIL

5) Non-metals are Dull

1) Most non-metals don't reflect light very well at all. Their surfaces are not usually as smooth as metals.
2) This makes them look dull.

Isn't carbon dull

carbon

6) Non-metals are Brittle

1) Non-metal structures are held together by weak forces.
2) This means they can shatter all too easily.

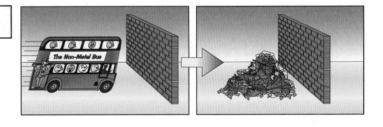

The Non-Metal Bus

7) Non-metals Have Low Melting Points and Boiling Points

1) The forces which hold the particles in non-metals together are very weak. This means they melt and boil very easily.
2) At room temperature, most non-metals are gases or solids. Only one is a liquid.

Non-Metal	State at Room Temperature	Melting Point (°C)	Boiling Point (°C)
Sulfur	Solid	113	445
Oxygen	Gas	-218	-183
Chlorine	Gas	-101	-35
Helium	Gas	-272	-269
Neon	Gas	-249	-246
Bromine	Liquid	-7	59

8) Non-metals *Have Low Densities*

1) Obviously the non-metals which are <u>gases</u> will have <u>very low density</u>.
   This means they don't have very many <u>particles</u> packed into a certain <u>space</u>.
   Some of these gases will even <u>float</u> in <u>air</u> — ideal for party balloons.

2) Even the liquid and solid non-metals have <u>low densities</u>.

9) Non-metals *are Not Magnetic*

1) Only a few <u>metals</u> like <u>iron</u>, <u>nickel</u>
   and <u>cobalt</u> are <u>magnetic</u>.

2) <u>All non-metals</u> are most definitely <u>non-magnetic</u>.

Proudly Perfect Properties of Non-metals Questions:

Quick Fire Questions

Q1 Which two things are non-metals usually poor conductors of?

Q2 Name three non-metals that are gases.

Q3 Name one non-metal that is a solid at room temperature.

Practice Questions

Q1 (a) Circle all the elements below that are **non-metals**.
             Use a periodic table to help you if you need it.

    Xe   Cu   Fe   Br   O   Mg   F

    Cl   C   I   Li   Pb   Ne   S

   (b) Some of the non-metal elements above are **gases** at room temperature. Name **three**.

   1. ....   2. ....   3. ....

Q2 Use the words in the boxes to fill in the gaps in the paragraph below.

| scrub | conduct | weak | forces | strong | break |

In most non-metals, the .... between the particles

are .... That's why non-metals .... easily.

They also wear away quickly because it's easy to .... molecules off them.

Q3 Read the following statements about non-metal elements.

> A   Non-metals are good thermal insulators.
>
> B   Non-metals bend easily without breaking.
>
> C   Non-metals fill about half of the Periodic Table.
>
> D   Non-metals are non-magnetic.
>
> E   All non-metals float in air.
>
> F   Most non-metals are gases at room temperature.

(a) Which **three** statements are correct? ....

(b) Use the space below to rewrite the other statements so that they are correct.

Letter .... Statement ....

....

Letter .... Statement ....

....

Letter .... Statement ....

....

Q4 Explain the following properties of non-metal elements.

(a) Low melting and boiling points

....

....

(b) Poor conductors of electricity

....

....

(c) Dull

....

....

Topic Review How did you get on with the questions?
Are you confident on the learning objective?

Section 1 — Classifying Materials

Properties of Other Materials

It's not just metals and non-metals that are <u>useful</u>. Other materials made from <u>compounds</u> or <u>mixtures of compounds</u> are handy too. After these pages, you will...

* be able to describe the <u>properties</u> of <u>polymers</u>, <u>ceramics</u> and <u>composites</u>.

Polymers *Have Many Useful Properties*

Polymers (that's <u>plastics</u> to you and me) include nylon, polythene and PVC.

1) Polymers are usually <u>insulators</u> of <u>heat</u> and <u>electricity</u>.
2) They're often <u>flexible</u> — they can be bent without breaking.
3) They have a <u>low density</u> — they can be very <u>light</u> for their size and strength. This makes them ideal for making things that need to be <u>strong</u> but <u>not heavy</u>.
4) They're <u>easily moulded</u> — they can be used to manufacture equipment with almost <u>any shape</u>.
5) Polymers are used to <u>make</u> things like...

Making polymers

1) Polymers are just <u>compounds</u> but they have <u>very long</u> molecules.
2) They're made by <u>joining</u> loads of little molecules together in <u>long chains</u>.
3) They usually contain <u>carbon</u> (a <u>non-metal</u>).

little molecules → chemical reaction → polymer chain

Kayaks

1) Polymers can easily be <u>moulded</u> into the <u>rounded</u> and <u>streamlined</u> shapes used in kayaks.
2) The <u>low density</u> of polymers means the kayak <u>floats</u> — which is handy.
3) Most polymers are also <u>waterproof</u> — again, good news for kayakers.

Carrier bags

1) A plastic carrier bag can <u>bend</u> and <u>stretch</u> without <u>breaking</u> — it's flexible.
2) This is good — it'd be pretty useless if it <u>snapped</u> or <u>crumbled</u> when you put a <u>tin of beans</u> in it.
3) It's also <u>light</u> for its strength.
4) It probably <u>won't biodegrade</u> (break down) very easily though — which is <u>bad news</u> for the <u>environment</u>.

Ceramics *are Stiff but Brittle*

Ceramics include glass, porcelain and bone china (for posh tea cups). They are:

1) <u>Insulators</u> of <u>heat</u> and <u>electricity</u>.
2) <u>Brittle</u> — they aren't very <u>flexible</u> and will <u>break</u> instead of <u>bending</u>.
3) <u>Stiff</u> — they can <u>withstand</u> strong forces before they break.
4) Because of these properties, ceramics are used where <u>high temperatures</u> or <u>strong forces</u> are involved, such as in...

Ceramics are made by 'baking' substances like <u>clay</u>.

Racing cars

1) Racing cars have <u>ceramic brake pads</u>.
2) When the driver pushes the brake pedal, the pad is <u>pressed</u> against the inside of the <u>wheel</u>. This <u>stops</u> the wheel <u>turning</u>.
3) The ceramic can withstand the <u>strong forces</u> and <u>high temperatures</u> generated by <u>friction</u> between the brake pad and the spinning wheel.

Ceramic brake pad

Composites are Made of Different Materials

1) Composite materials are made from two or more materials stuck together.

2) This can make a material with more useful properties than either material alone. For example:

Fibreglass

1) Fibreglass (or Glass Reinforced Plastic — GRP) consists of glass fibres embedded in plastic.

2) It has a low density (like plastic) but is very strong (like glass).

3) These properties mean fibreglass is used for things like skis, boats and surfboards.

Concrete

1) Concrete is made from a mixture of sand and gravel embedded in cement.

2) It can withstand high compression stresses (i.e. being squashed) so it's great at supporting heavy things.

3) This makes it ideal for use as a building material, for example in skate parks, shopping centres and airports.

Pretty Prickly Properties of Other Materials Questions:

Quick Fire Questions

Q1 What is another name for polymers?

Q2 Name one type of polymer.

Q3 Name one type of ceramic.

Practice Questions

Q1 Draw lines to match up the beginning of each sentence on the left with the correct ending on the right.

Polymers are usually...   ...strong forces before they break.

Ceramics are brittle, which means they are...   ...by joining molecules together in chains.

Ceramics can withstand...   ...not flexible.

Polymers are made...   ...by embedding glass fibres in plastic.

Fibreglass is made...   ...insulators of heat and electricity.

Q2 Would you use fibreglass or concrete to make each of the following objects? Explain your answers.

(a) a pair of skis ....

....

(b) a multi-storey car park ....

....

(c) a crash helmet ....

....

Challenge Yourself

Q3 Cherie has a composite material and a ceramic. She predicts that the ceramic will be better at insulating heat than the composite.

(a) In the space below, draw how Cherie could set up the equipment and materials on the right to test her prediction.

Your diagram doesn't have to be a work of art. Just make sure that the set up is clear.

Bunsen burner

temperature sensor

clamp and clamp stand

rod of material to be tested

heat-proof mat

(b) Describe how Cherie could carry out the experiment using the equipment you have drawn.

....

....

....

....

(c) Give **one** variable that Cherie will need to **control** in this experiment.

....

(d) Give **one** potential source of **random error** in this experiment.

....

Topic Review How did you feel about the questions? Have you understood the learning objective?

Section 1 — Classifying Materials

Chemical Reactions

Learning Objectives   In a chemical reaction, <u>atoms move</u> around into <u>new formations</u>. By the end of these pages you should know that...

• atoms in <u>reactants</u> rearrange to form <u>products</u>
• the <u>mass</u> of the <u>products</u> always <u>equals</u> the <u>mass</u> of the <u>reactants</u>.

Atoms Rearrange Themselves in a Chemical Reaction

1) In a <u>chemical reaction</u> atoms are <u>not</u> created or destroyed.
2) The atoms at the <u>start</u> of a reaction are <u>still there</u> at the <u>end</u>.
3) <u>Bonds</u> get <u>broken</u> and <u>made</u> in the reaction, as atoms <u>rearrange</u> themselves in going from the <u>reactants</u> to the <u>products</u> (p. 24). But the atoms themselves are <u>not altered</u>.

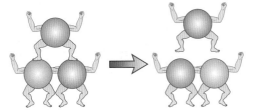

Take a look at this <u>example</u>:

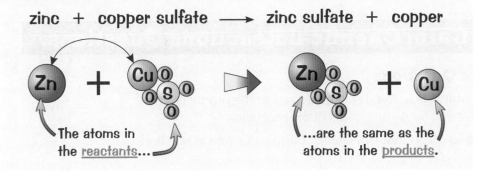

zinc + copper sulfate ⟶ zinc sulfate + copper

The atoms in the <u>reactants</u>...   ...are the same as the atoms in the <u>products</u>.

The Mass Doesn't Change in a Chemical Reaction

1) In a chemical reaction <u>no mass</u> is <u>lost</u> or <u>gained</u> when the <u>reactants</u> turn into the <u>products</u>.
2) This is because the <u>total number</u> of <u>atoms</u> is the <u>same</u> before and after the reaction.
3) Chemical reactions do involve a change in <u>energy</u>, i.e. reactions always <u>give out</u> or <u>take in</u> energy (p. 55). This is usually <u>heat</u> energy, which causes the <u>temperature</u> in a reaction to go up or down.
4) <u>Visible changes</u> can also occur in the reaction mixture. These show that a reaction has taken place. For example — a <u>gas</u> comes off, a <u>solid</u> is made, or the <u>colour</u> changes.

EXAMPLE: When <u>magnesium</u> reacts with <u>blue copper sulfate solution</u>, the solution goes <u>colourless</u>, <u>copper</u> coats the magnesium strip and the <u>temperature rises</u>. But the <u>mass</u> stays the <u>same</u>.

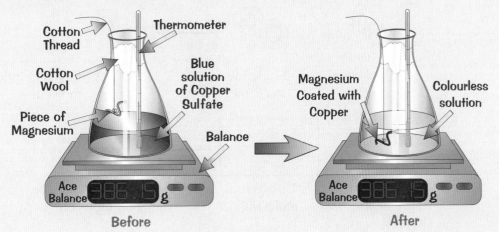

Cotton Thread   Thermometer
Cotton Wool
Blue solution of Copper Sulfate
Piece of Magnesium
Balance
Ace Balance 386.15 g
Before

Magnesium Coated with Copper   Colourless solution
Ace Balance 386.15 g
After

In chemical reactions that produce a <u>gas</u>, the mass in the <u>container</u> might <u>drop</u> as the gas <u>escapes</u>. The <u>total mass</u> of the products is <u>always equal</u> to the <u>total mass</u> of the reactants though.

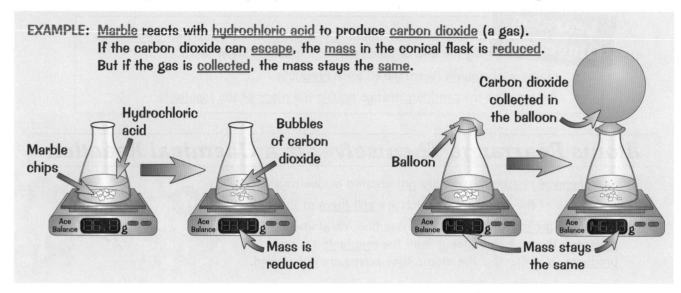

EXAMPLE: <u>Marble</u> reacts with <u>hydrochloric acid</u> to produce <u>carbon dioxide</u> (a gas). If the carbon dioxide can <u>escape</u>, the <u>mass</u> in the conical flask is <u>reduced</u>. But if the gas is <u>collected</u>, the mass stays the <u>same</u>.

Coolly Calm Chemical Reactions Questions:

Quick Fire Questions

Q1 In a chemical reaction, is the total mass of the products ever different to the total mass of the reactants?

Q2 Name two things that can change during a chemical reaction.

Practice Questions

Q1 Underline the **three** true sentences about chemical reactions:

A In chemical reactions, the atoms rearrange.

B Some atoms disappear in chemical reactions.

C There are the same numbers of atoms in the products as there are in the reactants.

D Atoms are joined together differently in the reactants than they are in the products.

E Atoms can change their mass in chemical reactions.

Q2 Draw **one** molecule in each box to show what happens in these chemical reactions.

(a)

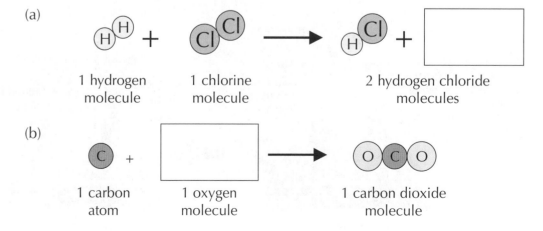

1 hydrogen molecule   1 chlorine molecule   2 hydrogen chloride molecules

(b)

1 carbon atom   1 oxygen molecule   1 carbon dioxide molecule

Q3 Look at the diagram, then complete the sentences below using words from the box.

| the same as | different to | 25 g | reactants | product | 27 g | 50 g |

Carol mixed 25 g of colourless sulfuric acid with 2 g of black copper oxide powder.

This produced .... of blue copper sulfate solution.

The total mass of the .... (what she started with) was

.... the mass of the .... (what she made).

Q4 Joseph heats a strip of zinc strongly in air, over a Bunsen burner.
The surface of the zinc becomes white. A white powder is quickly formed.

(a) Suggest **one** way in which Joseph can tell a reaction has happened.

....

(b) Safety is very important in this experiment.

(i) What should Joseph use to hold the zinc strip in the Bunsen flame?
Circle the correct answer below.

his fingers   **a piece of string**   **tongs**   **rubber gloves**

(ii) When Joseph has finished heating the zinc strip, what should he do to the Bunsen burner?

....

(iii) Why is it dangerous to wander off and leave a Bunsen burner on the blue flame?

....

....

Challenge Yourself

Q5 Look back at Joseph's experiment in **Q4**. The mass of the white powder at the end of the experiment is greater than the mass of the zinc strip at the start. Suggest a reason for this.

....

....

....

Topic Review How did you find the questions?
Are you happy with both of the learning objectives?

Examples of Chemical Reactions

There are loads of <u>different types</u> of chemical reactions. These pages will make sure you know all about...
- what's happening in <u>combustion</u>, <u>oxidation</u> and <u>thermal decomposition</u> reactions.

Combustion is Burning in Oxygen

1) Combustion is <u>burning</u> — a <u>fuel</u> reacts with <u>oxygen</u> (in the <u>air</u>) to release <u>energy</u>.

2) <u>Three</u> things are needed for combustion:

The oxygen usually comes from the air.

1) Fuel
2) Heat
3) Oxygen

3) <u>Hydrocarbons</u> are <u>fuels</u> containing only <u>hydrogen</u> and <u>carbon</u>. When there's enough <u>heat</u> and <u>oxygen</u>, hydrocarbons <u>combust</u> (burn) to give <u>water</u> and <u>carbon dioxide</u>:

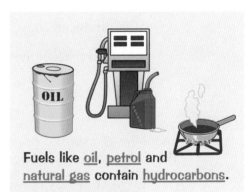
Fuels like <u>oil</u>, <u>petrol</u> and <u>natural gas</u> contain <u>hydrocarbons</u>.

hydrocarbon + oxygen ⟶ carbon dioxide + water (+ energy)

4) Combustion is useful because it gives off <u>energy</u> in the form of <u>heat</u> and <u>light</u>. It's the process behind candles, wood fires, car engines, coal power plants, etc.

Oxidation is the Gain of Oxygen

1) When a substance <u>reacts</u> and <u>combines</u> with <u>oxygen</u>, it's called an <u>oxidation</u> reaction.

2) <u>Combustion</u> is an oxidation reaction.

3) Another example of oxidation is <u>rusting</u>. <u>Iron</u> reacts with <u>oxygen</u> in the air to form <u>iron oxide</u>, i.e. <u>rust</u>.

iron + oxygen ⟶ iron oxide (rust)

You can say that the iron has been <u>oxidised</u>.

Thermal Decomposition is Breaking Down With Heat

1) <u>Thermal decomposition</u> is when a substance <u>breaks down</u> into at least two other substances when <u>heated</u>.

2) The substance <u>isn't</u> actually <u>reacting</u> with anything, but it <u>is</u> a <u>chemical</u> change.

3) Some <u>metal carbonates</u> break down on heating. Carbonates are substances with CO_3 in them, like copper(II) carbonate ($CuCO_3$) and zinc carbonate ($ZnCO_3$).

4) They break down into a <u>metal oxide</u> (e.g. copper oxide, CuO) and <u>carbon dioxide</u>. This usually results in a <u>colour change</u>.

It's too hot... I'm breaking down...

EXAMPLE: The thermal decomposition of copper(II) carbonate.

copper(II) carbonate ⟶ copper(II) oxide + carbon dioxide
$CuCO_3$ $\quad\quad$ CuO $\quad+\quad$ CO_2

This is <u>green</u>... ...and this is <u>black</u>.

Extra Exciting Examples (of Chemical Reactions) Questions:

Quick Fire Questions

Q1   What three things are needed for a combustion reaction to occur?

Q2   Give an example of an oxidation reaction.

Q3   What is thermal decomposition?

Practice Questions

Q1   (a)   Methane is a hydrocarbon. Complete this word equation
to show what happens when methane is burned:

methane + o…………..…...….. → ……...…..……   ……....…..…… + ……....…..……. + (energy)

(b)   This is a combustion reaction. What other type of reaction is it?

....

(c)   What is **useful** about this reaction?

....

Q2   A student heated solid **lead carbonate**, as shown in the diagram below.
It changed colour from white to yellow and a gas was given off.

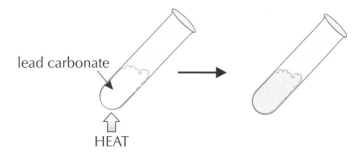

(a)   What type of reaction is this?

....

(b)   Suggest the name of the yellow product.

....

(c)   What was the gas produced by the reaction?

....

(d)   Write a word equation for this reaction.

....

Challenge Yourself

Q3 A group of pupils set up the experiment shown in the diagram.

Once they had lit the candle, they quickly placed the large glass container over it and timed how long the candle stayed alight.

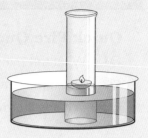

(a) After 29 seconds the candle went out. Suggest why.

....

(b) Suggest why the candle didn't go out as soon as the glass container was put over it.

....

Another group of pupils in the class burned a candle in a series of different-sized beakers, upside down. They timed how long the candle stayed alight in each one.

Here is a graph of their results:

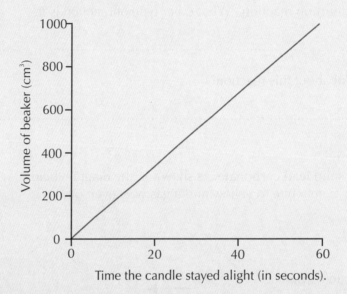

(c) What **relationship** does the graph show between the size of the beaker and the time the candle stayed alight?

....

(d) Use your scientific knowledge to explain **why** this relationship occurs.

....

....

(e) Use the graph to predict how long their candle would have stayed alight in a beaker of volume **2000 cm³**.

....

Topic Review   Did you feel confident answering the questions?
Are you sure you've got the learning objective sussed?

Section 2 — Chemical Changes

(b) (i) Which of the following terms could be used to describe the reaction of zinc with copper sulfate solution? Tick the correct box.

☐ exothermic   ☐ oxidation   ☐ decomposition   ☐ endothermic

(ii) Explain your answer to (i).

....

....

Q2 The decomposition of hydrogen peroxide produces a gas, oxygen. It is usually quite slow. The graph below shows the results of an experiment to find the best catalyst for this reaction. Three different catalysts were tested.

(a) How does a catalyst affect the energy needed to start a reaction?

....

....

(b) (i) What was the **dependent** variable in this experiment?

....

(ii) What was the **independent** variable in this experiment?

....

(iii) Give **two** control variables that needed to be kept the same in this experiment to make sure it was a fair test.

1. ....

2. ....

(c) Which was the best catalyst in this experiment? Explain your answer.

....

....

Topic Review How did you get on with the questions? Are you confident on the learning objectives?   😕 ☐   🙂 ☐   😃 ☐

Balancing Equations

Learning Objectives

Chemical equations tell you what's <u>reacting</u>, what's being <u>made</u> and <u>how much</u> <u>reactant</u> and <u>product</u> you've got. Phew. By the end of these pages you should...

- be able to write <u>chemical reactions</u> as <u>equations</u> using <u>words</u> and <u>symbols</u>
- know how to <u>balance</u> symbol equations.

Chemical Equations Show What Happens in a Reaction

You can show what happens in a chemical reaction using:

1) A <u>WORD EQUATION</u> — where the <u>names</u> of the products and reactants are written out in <u>full</u>.

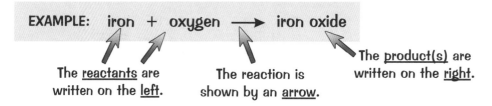

EXAMPLE: iron + oxygen ⟶ iron oxide

The <u>reactants</u> are written on the <u>left</u>.

The reaction is shown by an <u>arrow</u>.

The <u>product(s)</u> are written on the <u>right</u>.

2) A <u>SYMBOL EQUATION</u> — which uses <u>chemical symbols</u> (page 19) and <u>formulae</u> (page 25).
   A <u>balanced</u> symbol equation shows <u>how many</u> of each chemical react or are made in a reaction.

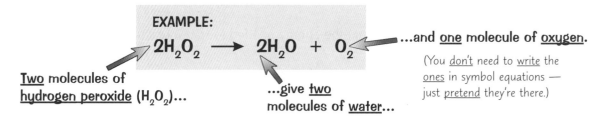

EXAMPLE:

$$2H_2O_2 \longrightarrow 2H_2O + O_2$$

<u>Two</u> molecules of <u>hydrogen peroxide</u> (H_2O_2)...

...give <u>two</u> molecules of <u>water</u>...

...and <u>one</u> molecule of <u>oxygen</u>.

(You <u>don't</u> need to <u>write</u> the <u>ones</u> in symbol equations — just <u>pretend</u> they're there.)

Chemical Equations are Equal on Both Sides

The number of <u>atoms</u> stays the <u>same</u> throughout a reaction (see p. 49), so a balanced symbol equation should show the <u>same number</u> of <u>atoms</u> on <u>each side</u>.
Here's an example of writing a <u>balanced equation</u> for burning magnesium in oxygen.

1) Write the <u>word equation</u>:   magnesium + oxygen ⟶ magnesium oxide

2) Write in the <u>chemical formulae</u> of all the reactants and products: $Mg + O_2 \longrightarrow MgO$

3) Check that the equation is <u>balanced</u> by <u>counting</u> the number of <u>each atom</u> on <u>both sides</u> of the equation.
   Then do steps A, B, C and D below and on the next page to <u>balance</u> the atoms up one by one.
   Keep track of the <u>number</u> of atoms on <u>each side</u> as you go:

Oxygen gas is made up of pairs of atoms, called molecules — that's why it's O_2.

Left side of equation	Right side of equation
One Magnesium	One Magnesium
Two Oxygen	One Oxygen

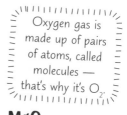

A Find an element that doesn't balance and pencil in a big number to try and sort it out.
There isn't enough <u>oxygen</u> on the <u>right side</u> of the equation — add "<u>2</u>" before MgO.

$$Mg + O_2 \longrightarrow 2MgO$$

2MgO means 2 Mg atoms <u>and</u> 2 O atoms.

You can't change a chemical formula just to make it fit. E.g. O_2 can't become O here.

B See where that gets you by counting up the atoms again.

Left side of equation	Right side of equation
One Magnesium	Two Magnesium
Two Oxygen	Two Oxygen

C Continue to chase the unbalanced atoms by going back to A — pencil in a number before a formula, then see where it gets you when you count up the atoms.

There isn't enough <u>magnesium</u> on the <u>left side</u> of the equation — add a "<u>2</u>" before Mg.

$$2Mg + O_2 \longrightarrow 2MgO$$

D See where that gets you by counting up the atoms again.

Left side of equation	Right side of equation
Two Magnesium	Two Magnesium
Two Oxygen	Two Oxygen

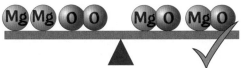

Done and dusted.

Bizarrely Beautiful Balancing Equations Questions:

Quick Fire Questions

Q1 On what side of a chemical equation are the reactants written?

Q2 Which of the equations below is correctly balanced?

    A $Na + H_2O \rightarrow 2NaOH + H_2$

    B $Fe + O_2 \rightarrow FeO_2$

Q3 Why should symbol equations be balanced?

Practice Questions

Q1 (a) Copper reacts with oxygen to give copper oxide. Write a word equation for this reaction.

....

    (b) When sodium is mixed with water, they react to make sodium hydroxide and hydrogen. Write a word equation for this reaction.

....

Q2 (a) Complete the word equation below.

.... + chlorine → sodium chloride

    (b) Complete the balanced symbol equation for this reaction using the correct numbers and symbols:

        $2............ + Cl_2 \rightarrow ....NaCl$

Q3 Sulfur burns in air to give sulfur dioxide (SO_2).
Write a symbol equation for this reaction.

....

Q4 Balance the following symbol equations:

(a) $C + O_2 \rightarrow CO$

....

(b) $K + Br_2 \rightarrow KBr$

....

(c) $Mg + HCl \rightarrow MgCl_2 + H_2$

....

(d) $NaOH + H_2SO_4 \rightarrow Na_2SO_4 + H_2O$

....

(e) $Fe + Cl_2 \rightarrow FeCl_3$

....

Challenge Yourself

Q5 Lithium reacts with water to give lithium hydroxide (LiOH) and hydrogen gas.
Write a balanced symbol equation for this reaction.

....

Q6 Nitrogen reacts with hydrogen to make ammonia. The equation for this reaction is shown below.

$$N_2 + 3H_2 \rightarrow 2NH_3$$

(a) If **two** molecules of nitrogen react with hydrogen,
how many molecules of **ammonia** would be produced?

Answer: ....

(b) If **three** molecules of nitrogen react, how many
molecules of **hydrogen** would they react with?

Answer: ....

Topic Review How did you find the questions?
Are you happy with the learning objectives?

Section 2 — Chemical Changes

Reactivity Series and Metal Extraction

Learning Objectives

Some <u>metals</u> are <u>more reactive</u> than others. We can <u>order</u> them by their <u>reactivity</u>. By the end of these pages you should...

- know the <u>order</u> of <u>metals</u> in the <u>reactivity series</u>
- know where <u>carbon</u> fits in the <u>reactivity series</u> (and <u>hydrogen</u>)
- understand how <u>carbon</u> can be used to <u>extract metals</u> from <u>metal oxides</u>.

The Reactivity Series — How Well a Metal Reacts

The <u>reactivity series</u> lists metals in <u>order</u> of their <u>reactivity</u> towards other substances.

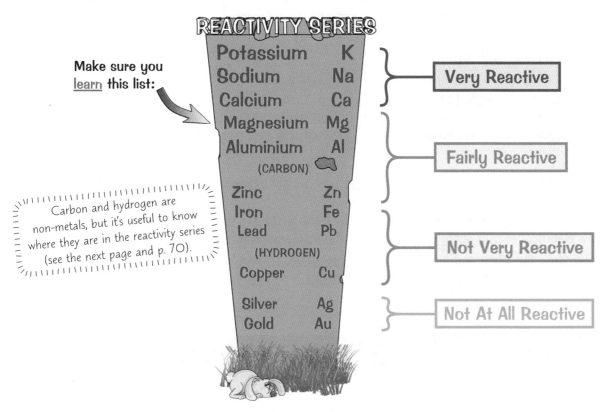

Make sure you <u>learn</u> this list:

Carbon and hydrogen are non-metals, but it's useful to know where they are in the reactivity series (see the next page and p. 70).

REACTIVITY SERIES

Potassium	K	Very Reactive
Sodium	Na	
Calcium	Ca	
Magnesium	Mg	Fairly Reactive
Aluminium	Al	
(CARBON)		
Zinc	Zn	Not Very Reactive
Iron	Fe	
Lead	Pb	
(HYDROGEN)		
Copper	Cu	
Silver	Ag	Not At All Reactive
Gold	Au	

The <u>higher</u> a metal is in the <u>reactivity series</u>, the more <u>quickly</u> or <u>violently</u> it <u>reacts</u>.

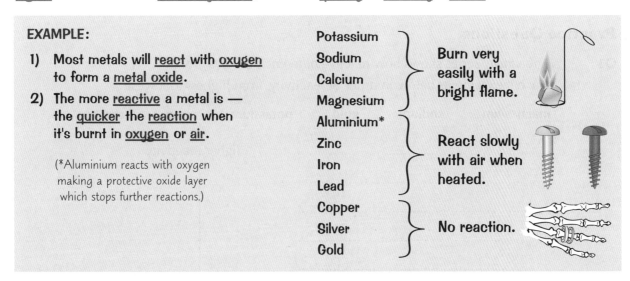

EXAMPLE:

1) Most metals will <u>react</u> with <u>oxygen</u> to form a <u>metal oxide</u>.

2) The more <u>reactive</u> a metal is — the <u>quicker</u> the <u>reaction</u> when it's burnt in <u>oxygen</u> or <u>air</u>.

(*Aluminium reacts with oxygen making a protective oxide layer which stops further reactions.)

Potassium
Sodium
Calcium
Magnesium } Burn very easily with a bright flame.

Aluminium*
Zinc
Iron
Lead } React slowly with air when heated.

Copper
Silver
Gold } No reaction.

You can <u>use</u> the <u>reactivity series</u> to make <u>predictions</u> about how <u>metals</u> will <u>behave</u> in <u>different reactions</u>. See pages 70 and 75 for more.

Some Metals Can Be Extracted With Carbon

1) Metals are usually mined as <u>ores</u> — rocks containing different <u>metals</u> and <u>metal compounds</u> (usually <u>metal oxides</u> — see page 73).

2) A metal can be <u>extracted</u> from its ore by <u>reduction</u> using <u>carbon</u>. When an ore is reduced, <u>oxygen is removed</u> from it — leaving the isolated <u>metal</u> behind.

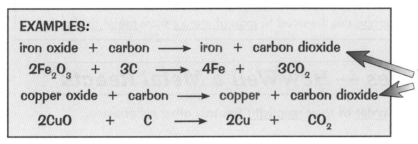

EXAMPLES:

iron oxide + carbon ⟶ iron + carbon dioxide

$2Fe_2O_3 + 3C \longrightarrow 4Fe + 3CO_2$

copper oxide + carbon ⟶ copper + carbon dioxide

$2CuO + C \longrightarrow 2Cu + CO_2$

The <u>carbon</u> joins with the <u>oxygen</u> to form <u>carbon dioxide</u>.

How it's Done — IRON:

<u>Iron</u> is made <u>commercially</u> by <u>reducing</u> iron oxide in a <u>blast furnace</u> (a <u>really hot</u> oven). The <u>iron ore</u> is mixed with <u>coke</u> (a solid fuel that contains <u>carbon</u>) at <u>high temperatures</u>. The <u>carbon</u> in the coke <u>removes</u> the oxygen from the ore.

3) Only metals that are <u>less reactive</u> than <u>carbon</u> (i.e. metals <u>below</u> carbon in the reactivity series) can be extracted from their ore using carbon.

4) Metals that are <u>more reactive</u> than carbon need to be extracted using <u>electrolysis</u> (where electrical energy <u>splits up</u> the ore into the elements that make it up).

5) Some metals, like silver and gold, are pretty <u>unreactive</u>, so they're often found in their <u>pure form</u> — i.e. <u>not chemically combined</u> with <u>other elements</u> in an <u>ore</u>.

Roly Poly Reactivity Series (and Metal Extraction) Questions:

Quick Fire Question

Q1 Which of these metals will react the most violently with oxygen — aluminium, sodium or zinc?

Practice Questions

Q1 A reactivity series shows how reactive different elements are.

(a) Place the elements below in order of reactivity, from highest to lowest.

magnesium   **sodium**   **gold**   **potassium**   **iron**   **carbon**

1 ....   Higher reactivity

2 ....

3 ....

4 ....

5 ....

6 ....   Lower reactivity

(b) Which of the elements listed in part (a) is a non-metal?

....

(c) Suggest a way that you could **test** the metals **sodium**
and **iron** to show which one is more reactive?

....

Q2 Iron and calcium are found as ores.

(a) (i) Iron can be extracted from its ore using carbon. What type of reaction is this?

....

(ii) Write the **word** equation for the reaction between iron oxide and carbon.

....

(iii) The reaction between iron oxide and carbon is usually carried out
at very high temperatures. Suggest why.

....

(b) Calcium can only be extracted from its ore by melting and electrolysis.
Explain why.

....

....

(c) Apart from iron, name **two** other metals that can be extracted from their ores by carbon.

1 .... 2 ....

Challenge Yourself

Q3 **Iron** has been known about and used for thousands of years.
However, we have only known about and used **aluminium** for around two hundred years.

Use your scientific knowledge about extracting metals from their ores to suggest
a possible reason for this.

....

....

....

Topic Review How did you find the questions?
Are you confident on all the learning objectives?

Reactions of Metals with Acids

If you don't remember the <u>reactivity series</u> (on p. 67), flick back there <u>now</u>. It's <u>dead important</u> for these pages. By the end of this topic you should...
* know how <u>acids</u> react with <u>metals</u> to give a <u>salt</u> and <u>hydrogen</u>.

Reacting Metals With Dilute Acid

$$\text{metal} + \text{acid} \longrightarrow \text{salt} + \text{hydrogen}$$

All acids contain hydrogen — so the hydrogen here comes from the acid.

1) Metals above <u>hydrogen</u> in the <u>reactivity series</u> will <u>react</u> with <u>acids</u> to make a <u>salt</u> and <u>hydrogen</u>. The hydrogen is released as a <u>gas</u>.

2) The metals <u>below</u> hydrogen in the <u>reactivity series don't react</u> with <u>acids</u>.

3) The reaction becomes <u>less and less exciting</u> as you go <u>down</u> the <u>series</u>.

More Reactive Metals React More Violently

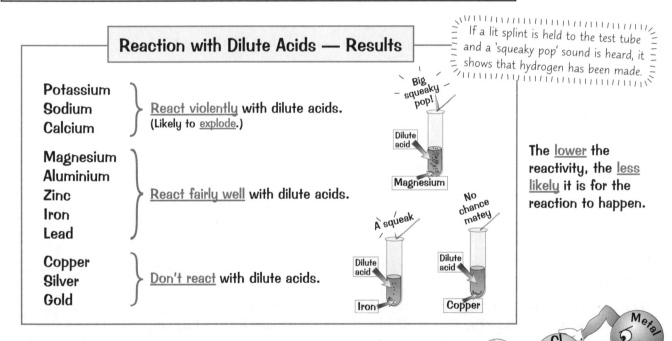

Reaction with Dilute Acids — Results

If a lit splint is held to the test tube and a 'squeaky pop' sound is heard, it shows that hydrogen has been made.

Potassium
Sodium
Calcium
} <u>React violently</u> with dilute acids. (Likely to <u>explode</u>.)

Magnesium
Aluminium
Zinc
Iron
Lead
} <u>React fairly well</u> with dilute acids.

Copper
Silver
Gold
} <u>Don't react</u> with dilute acids.

The <u>lower</u> the reactivity, the <u>less likely</u> it is for the reaction to happen.

EXAMPLES:

a) zinc + sulfuric acid $\longrightarrow$ zinc sulfate + hydrogen
   Zn + H_2SO_4 $\longrightarrow$ $ZnSO_4$ + H_2

Holy shamoly

The zinc <u>takes the place</u> of the hydrogen in the acid because it's <u>more reactive</u> than the hydrogen.

b) sodium + hydrochloric acid $\longrightarrow$ sodium chloride + hydrogen
   $2Na$ + $2HCl$ $\longrightarrow$ $2NaCl$ + H_2

The sodium <u>takes the place</u> of the hydrogen in the acid — again because it's <u>more reactive</u> than the hydrogen.

Ready-Made Reactions of Metals (with Acids) Questions:

Quick Fire Questions

Q1 Which of these metals reacts more violently with a dilute acid — sodium or magnesium?

Q2 Name one metal in the reactivity series that will not react with dilute acid.

Q3 How could you test whether the reaction between a metal and an acid produces hydrogen?

Practice Questions

Q1 Elena puts samples of copper, magnesium and zinc into test tubes and adds dilute sulfuric acid to each one. The diagram below shows what happens.

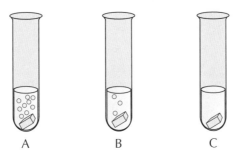

A   B   C

(a) Elena has taken steps to make sure she can compare the reactions fairly. Suggest **two** steps she may have taken.

1 ....

2 ....

(b) Which test tube is most likely to contain **copper**: A, B or C? Explain your answer.

....

....

(c) What do the bubbles in test tubes A and B tell you about the reactivity of the metals in these test tubes?

....

....

....

....

(d) (i) Complete the equation below to give the **general** equation for the reaction of a metal with dilute acid.

metal + acid ⟶ ....

(ii) Which test tube contains magnesium, A, B or C? ....

(iii) Write down the **word** equation for the reaction between magnesium and sulfuric acid.

....

Section 2 — Chemical Changes

Q2 A simple hydrogen gas generator is shown below. Paul decides to carry out three experiments with three different metals to see which one will generate hydrogen fastest.

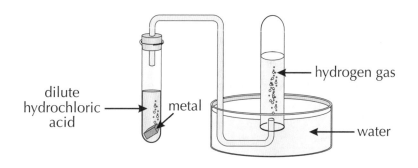

(a) He quickly decides **not** to use the following metals in his experiments. Suggest why.

(i) copper

....

....

(ii) potassium, sodium or calcium

....

....

(b) Paul decides to use magnesium, iron and zinc in his experiments. Which metal would you expect to produce hydrogen **fastest** — magnesium, iron or zinc?

....

(c) Paul repeated his experiment three times for each metal. Explain why he did this.

....

....

(d) Paul's teacher asks him to put together a reactivity series for five more metals. They all react safely with acid.

Describe how Paul could use his gas generator to find out the reactivity of the different metals.

....

....

....

Topic Review How did you get on with the questions? Are you happy with the learning objective?

Section 2 — Chemical Changes

Reactions of Oxides with Acids

An <u>oxide</u> is a <u>compound</u> with <u>oxygen</u> joined to <u>one other element</u>. Easy as that. By the end of these pages you should...
*   know that <u>metal oxides</u> are <u>alkaline</u> and will <u>neutralise</u> an <u>acid</u>
*   know that <u>non-metal oxides</u> are <u>acidic</u> and will <u>neutralise</u> an <u>alkali</u>.

Metals React With Oxygen to Make Oxides

1) Most metals react with <u>oxygen</u> to make <u>metal oxides</u>.

   E.g. magnesium + oxygen → magnesium oxide.

2) The metal oxides formed are always <u>solids</u>.
3) How <u>quickly</u> a metal reacts with oxygen depends on how <u>reactive</u> it is (see p. 67).
4) Some <u>unreactive</u> metals, like <u>gold</u>, will <u>not react</u> with oxygen at all.

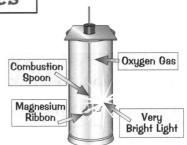

Metal Oxides are Alkaline

1) Some metal oxides will <u>dissolve</u> in <u>water</u> to form a <u>solution</u>.
2) Metal oxides in solution have a <u>pH</u> which is <u>higher than 7</u> — i.e. they're <u>alkaline</u> (see p. 61).
3) So <u>metal oxides</u> can be reacted with <u>acids</u> to make a <u>salt</u> and <u>water</u>. This is a <u>neutralisation reaction</u> — see page 64.

   acid + metal oxide ⟶ salt + water

4) Metal oxides that <u>don't dissolve</u> in water will still neutralise acids.

EXAMPLES:
hydrochloric acid + copper oxide → copper chloride + water
sulfuric acid + zinc oxide → zinc sulfate + water
nitric acid + magnesium oxide → magnesium nitrate + water

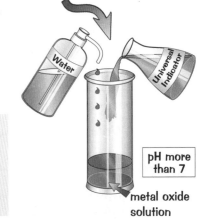

Non-metals React With Oxygen to Make Oxides

1) Non-metals also react with <u>oxygen</u> to make <u>oxides</u>.

   EXAMPLES: sulfur + oxygen → sulfur dioxide
   carbon + oxygen → carbon dioxide

2) Many non-metal oxides are <u>gases</u>.

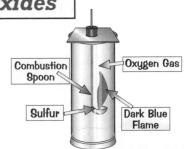

Non-metal *Oxides are Acidic*

1) Most non-metal oxides have a <u>pH below 7</u> when dissolved in water. This means they're <u>acidic</u>.

2) So <u>non-metal oxides</u> will react with alkalis to make a <u>salt</u> and <u>water</u>.

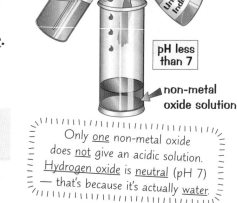

pH less than 7

non-metal oxide solution

alkali + non-metal oxide $\longrightarrow$ salt + water

EXAMPLE:
sodium hydroxide + silicon dioxide $\rightarrow$ sodium silicate + water

an alkali   a non-metal oxide

Only <u>one</u> non-metal oxide does <u>not</u> give an acidic solution. <u>Hydrogen oxide</u> is <u>neutral</u> (pH 7) — that's because it's actually <u>water</u>.

Really Rad Reactions of Oxides (with Acids) Questions:

Quick Fire Questions

Q1 What two reactants would you need to form a metal oxide?

Q2 A metal oxide and a non-metal oxide are dissolved in water. Which solution has the highest pH?

Practice Questions

Q1 When sodium burns it reacts with oxygen in the air.

(a) Write a **word** equation for the reaction of sodium with oxygen.

....

(b) The product of this reaction is an **alkali**. What will happen when this product reacts with an acid?

....

Q2 Josie carries out an experiment in which sulfur burns in oxygen.

(a) Write a **word** equation for the reaction of sulfur with oxygen.

....

(b) Josie dissolves the product of this reaction in water. What can you say about the pH value of this solution? ....

Q3 (a) Write a **balanced symbol** equation for the reaction that takes place when magnesium burns.

....

(b) Tina adds dilute sulfuric acid to the product of this reaction.

(i) Name the **type** of reaction that will take place. ....

(ii) Name the **salt** that Tina will make. ....

Topic Review Did you feel confident answering the questions? Have you got the learning objectives sussed?

Displacement Reactions

Learning Objective

Displacement is a fancy way of saying something is being replaced by something else. By the end of these pages you should...

• understand how displacement reactions work.

'Displacement' Means 'Taking the Place of'

A more reactive metal will displace a less reactive metal from its compound.

1) The reactivity series (see page 67) tells you which are the most reactive metals — i.e. the ones which react most strongly with other things.

2) If you put a more reactive metal like magnesium into a solution of a less reactive metal compound, like copper sulfate, then magnesium will take the place of the copper — and make magnesium sulfate.

3) The "kicked out" metal then coats itself on the reactive metal, so we'd see copper.

4) This only happens if the metal added is more reactive — higher displaces lower. Got it?

A Reactivity Series Investigation

You can use displacement reactions to investigate the reactivity of metals.

Method: 1) Slap a bit of metal into some salt solutions.   2) See what happens.

Here's what you need to start with:

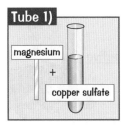
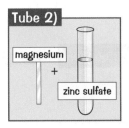
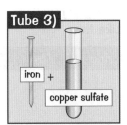
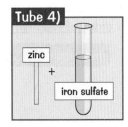
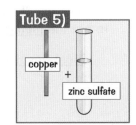

And here's what happens when you add the metals to the salt solutions:

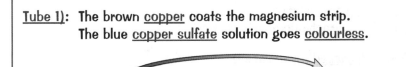

Tube 1): The brown copper coats the magnesium strip.
The blue copper sulfate solution goes colourless.

magnesium + copper sulfate ⟶ magnesium sulfate + copper

Magnesium takes the place of copper in the sulfate compound.
So magnesium must be more reactive than copper.

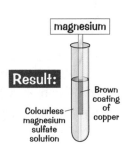

Result: Brown coating of copper. Colourless magnesium sulfate solution. magnesium

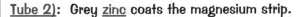

Tube 2): Grey zinc coats the magnesium strip.

magnesium + zinc sulfate ⟶ magnesium sulfate + zinc

Magnesium takes the place of zinc in the sulfate compound.
So magnesium must be more reactive than zinc.

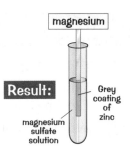

Result: Grey coating of zinc. magnesium sulfate solution. magnesium

<u>Tube 3):</u> The brown <u>copper</u> coats the nail.
The blue <u>copper sulfate</u> solution goes <u>green</u>.

iron + copper sulfate ⟶ iron sulfate + copper

Iron <u>takes the place</u> of copper in the sulfate compound.
So <u>iron</u> must be <u>more reactive</u> than copper.

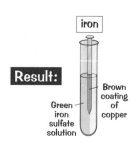

Result:

Brown coating of copper

Green iron sulfate solution

iron

<u>Tube 4:</u> Grey <u>iron</u> is seen coating the zinc strip.
The green <u>iron sulfate</u> solution goes <u>colourless</u>.

zinc + iron sulfate ⟶ zinc sulfate + iron

Zinc <u>takes the place</u> of iron in the sulfate compound.
So <u>zinc</u> must be <u>more reactive</u> than iron.

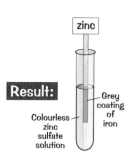

Result:

Grey coating of iron

Colourless zinc sulfate solution

zinc

<u>Tube 5):</u> There's <u>no reaction</u>.
Copper <u>can't displace</u> zinc — it's <u>not reactive</u> enough.

Nope.

copper + zinc sulfate ⟶ no change

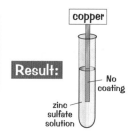

Result:

No coating

zinc sulfate solution

copper

You can use the <u>results</u> of all these <u>displacement reactions</u>
to put the <u>metals</u> in <u>order of reactivity</u>. Like this:

<u>Most Reactive</u> | magnesium   zinc   iron   copper | <u>Least Reactive</u>

Neutralisation **is a** *Displacement Reaction*

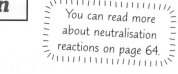

You can read more about neutralisation reactions on page 64.

There are lots of <u>different types</u> of <u>displacement reactions</u>.
The <u>neutralisation</u> of <u>sodium hydroxide</u> by <u>hydrochloric acid</u> is also one.

1) The <u>hydrogen</u> in hydrochloric acid is <u>displaced</u> (or replaced)
by <u>sodium</u> from the <u>sodium hydroxide</u> (the alkali).

2) This makes <u>NaCl</u> and <u>H_2O</u>.

3) NaCl is <u>sodium chloride</u> — common salt.
And of course H_2O is <u>water</u>. Of course you knew.

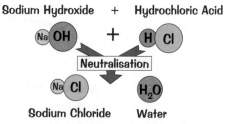

Sodium Hydroxide + Hydrochloric Acid

Na OH   +   H Cl

Neutralisation

Na Cl H_2O

Sodium Chloride   Water

Doubly Delightful Displacement Reactions Questions:

Quick Fire Questions

Q1 Describe what you would see if magnesium was added to copper sulfate solution.
Explain your answer.

Q2 Why is neutralisation a displacement reaction?

Practice Questions

Q1 Callum is investigating the reactivity of four metals, nickel, palladium, copper and mercury.
He sets up five test tubes, each containing a sample of metal and a salt solution, and observes
them to see if a displacement reaction takes place. His results are shown in the table below.

Test tube	Metal	Salt solution	Displacement reaction?
1	mercury	palladium nitrate	yes
2	copper	mercury nitrate	yes
3	nickel	copper sulfate	yes
4	palladium	copper sulfate	no

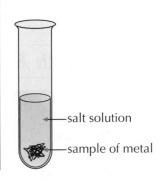
—salt solution
—sample of metal

(a) Describe **two** changes that would tell Callum a displacement reaction
has taken place in **test tube 3**.

1 ....

2 ....

(b) List the metals in order of reactivity, with the most reactive first.

1 .... Most reactive

2 ....

3 ....

4 .... Least reactive

(c) (i) Complete the following equation to show the reaction happening in test tube 2.

copper + mercury nitrate ⟶ ....

(ii) Which test tube is the following reaction taking place in?

$$Ni + CuSO_4 \longrightarrow NiSO_4 + Cu$$ **Test tube** ....

(d) Callum wants to add chromium to his reactivity series.
He thinks chromium is more reactive than any of the metals in his list.

(i) What could Callum react chromium with to prove this? ....

(ii) Write the word equation for the reaction.

....

The Earth's Structure

Learning Objectives

The Earth isn't solid rock all the way through — if you broke it open*, you'd find different layers inside. After reading this page, you should know...

- how the Earth is structured — including what it looks like on the inside
- what the Earth is made of.

The Earth Has a Crust, a Mantle and a Core

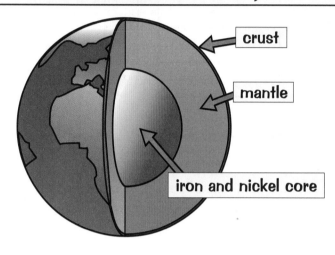

crust

mantle

iron and nickel core

The Earth is almost a sphere and it has a layered structure. A bit like a scotch egg. Or a peach.

1) We live on the crust — a thin, outer layer of solid rock.

2) Below that is the mantle.

3) The mantle is mostly solid, but deep down it can flow very slowly (like a liquid). This is because the temperature increases as you go deeper into the mantle.

4) At the centre of the Earth is the core. We think it's made of iron and nickel.

The Crust Contains Minerals

Elements and compounds make up minerals — and these make up rocks in the crust. E.g.

Elements	Compound	Mineral	Rock
Silicon & Oxygen	Silicon dioxide	Quartz	Granite

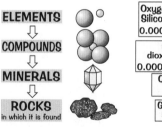

ELEMENTS
⇩
COMPOUNDS
⇩
MINERALS
⇩
ROCKS
in which it is found

Oxygen (O) Silicon (Si) 0.000000014 cm	Well Small
Silicon dioxide (SiO$_2$) 0.000000024 cm	Small
Quartz 1 cm	Visible
Granite 5 cm	Rather Large

The Earth's Surface is Made Up of Tectonic Plates

1) The crust and the upper part of the mantle are cracked into a number of large pieces. These pieces are called tectonic plates.

2) Tectonic plates are a bit like big rafts that 'float' on the mantle. They're able to move around.

3) The map shows the edges of the plates as they are now, and the directions they're moving in (red arrows).

4) Most of the plates are moving very slowly (a few centimetres a year).

5) Sometimes, the plates move very suddenly, causing an earthquake.

6) Volcanoes and earthquakes often happen where two tectonic plates meet.

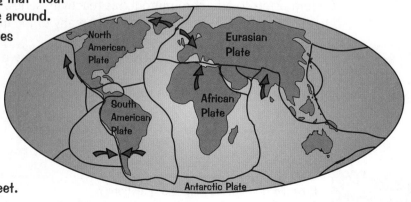

North American Plate

Eurasian Plate

South American Plate

African Plate

Antarctic Plate

*CGP cannot be held responsible for the destruction of the Earth.

Easily Enlightening Earth's Structure Questions:

Quick Fire Questions

Q1 What is the name for the Earth's thin outer layer of solid rock?

Q2 What are tectonic plates? Roughly how fast do the Earth's tectonic plates move?

Q3 Give two things that can happen where two tectonic plates meet.

Practice Questions

Q1 Use the words in the box to fill in the gaps in the paragraph below.

compound	rocks	oxygen	elements

Quartz is a mineral that is found in the .... that make up the Earth's crust.

Quartz is made up of silicon dioxide, which is a ....

Silicon dioxide contains the .... silicon and ....

Q2 The diagram on the right shows what scientists think a cross-section of the planet **Mars** might look like.

crust

mantle

iron and sulfur core

(a) Using the diagram to help you, write down **two** similarities between the structures of **Earth** and **Mars**.

1. ....

....

2. ....

(b) Write down **one** difference between the structures of Earth and Mars.

....

(c) Scientists have noticed that some boulders on the surface of Mars have rolled downhill, leaving marks in the surface behind them. They think that 'marsquakes' made the boulders roll.

Fill in the gaps in the sentences below using some of these words:
guessed, evidence, observed, investigation and **hypothesis**. (WS)

The scientists .... that boulders have rolled downhill.

They came up with the .... that the boulders started to roll

due to 'marsquakes'. In order for their theory to become accepted, they need to

collect more .... to support it.

Topic Review How did you get on with the questions?
Are you confident on the learning objectives?

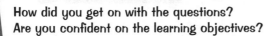

Section 3 — The Earth and The Atmosphere

Rock Types

Rocks are like chocolates — there are <u>different types</u> and they'll ruin your teeth. After these pages, you should...

- know the key differences between <u>igneous</u>, <u>sedimentary</u> and <u>metamorphic</u> rocks
- be able to explain how each type of rock is <u>formed</u>.

There are Three Different Types of Rock

1) Igneous Rocks

1) These are formed from <u>magma</u> (melted underground rock) which is pushed up to the surface of the crust — and often out through <u>volcanoes</u>.

2) They contain various <u>minerals</u> in randomly-arranged <u>interlocking crystals</u>.

3) The <u>size</u> of the <u>crystals</u> (or texture) depends on how <u>quickly</u> the magma <u>cools</u>. <u>Large crystals</u> form when magma cools <u>slowly</u>. <u>Small crystals</u> are made when it cools <u>rapidly</u>.

4) There are <u>two types</u> of igneous rocks: <u>extrusive</u> and <u>intrusive</u>.

Extrusive igneous rocks — cool <u>quickly</u> <u>above ground</u>.

Intrusive igneous rocks — cool <u>slowly</u> <u>underground</u> and eventually get exposed when rocks above them wear away.

5) Here are some <u>examples</u> of the different types of igneous rock:

Granite

1) Granite is an <u>intrusive</u> igneous rock. It's formed when magma <u>pushes up</u> into the crust, but doesn't make it to the <u>surface</u>.

2) The magma <u>cools slowly</u> underground and forms <u>large mineral crystals</u>.

3) The different <u>colours</u> in granite are <u>crystals</u> of different minerals.

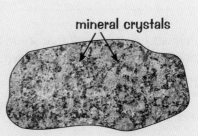

mineral crystals

Basalt

1) Basalt is an <u>extrusive</u> igneous rock. It is formed when magma <u>erupts</u> out of volcanoes.

2) The liquid magma cools <u>rapidly</u> into a solid — so there's <u>not much time</u> for crystals to <u>grow</u>.

3) As a result, the crystals in basalt are quite <u>small</u>.

liquid magma

solid basalt

2) Sedimentary Rocks

1) These are formed from <u>layers</u> of <u>sediment</u> (rock fragments or dead matter) laid down in <u>lakes</u> or <u>seas</u> over <u>millions</u> of years.

2) Sedimentary rocks can also form when water evaporates and leaves a <u>dissolved solid</u> (like salt) behind.

3) The layers are <u>cemented</u> together by <u>other minerals</u>.

Sandstone

1) Sandstone is a <u>sedimentary rock</u> formed from <u>layers of sand</u>.

2) It is used for <u>building</u> because it's relatively <u>soft</u> — so it's easy to work with.

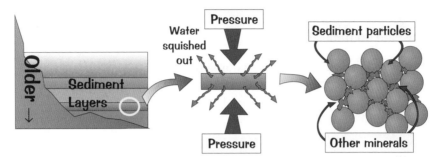

4) <u>Fossils</u> can form in the sediments. These are the <u>remains</u> of dead <u>plants</u> and <u>animals</u>, which have turned into <u>minerals</u> over millions of years. The <u>type</u> of fossil can be used to work out the <u>relative age</u> of the rock.

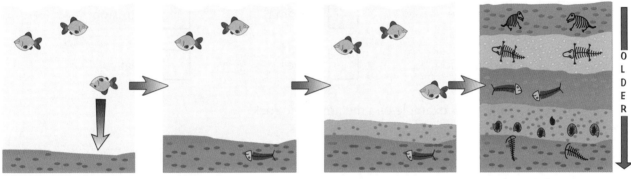

An animal dies and falls to the <u>sea floor</u>.

Its remains are <u>buried</u> by sediment.

Over time, the layers of sediment turn into <u>sedimentary rock</u>.

Each rock layer contains <u>fossils</u> of animals and plants that lived when the sediment layer formed.

3) Metamorphic Rocks

1) These are the result of <u>heat</u> and <u>increased pressure</u> acting on existing rocks over <u>long</u> periods of time.

2) They may have really <u>tiny crystals</u> and some (like slate) have <u>layers</u>.

3) The kind of metamorphic rock that's formed depends on what <u>original rock</u> was. For example:

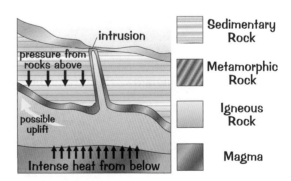

Marble

1) <u>Limestone</u> is a kind of <u>sedimentary</u> rock. When limestone gets buried <u>deep underground</u>, it is subjected to increased <u>pressure</u> and <u>heat</u>.

2) This turns limestone into a <u>metamorphic</u> rock called <u>marble</u>.

3) Marble sometimes has different-coloured <u>minerals</u> in it.

<u>Slate</u> is a metamorphic rock often used for <u>roof tiles</u>. The <u>layering</u> in the rock makes it easy to <u>split</u> into <u>thin sheets</u>.

Section 3 — The Earth and The Atmosphere

Rather Rocking Rock Types Questions:

Quick Fire Questions

Q1 What are the two types of igneous rock?

Q2 What is magma?

Q3 Which kind of rock is most likely to contain fossils?

Practice Questions

Q1 Slate and schist are both metamorphic rocks.

    (a) 'Metamorphic' is another word for 'changed'.
Explain why 'metamorphic' is an appropriate name for this type of rock.

....

....

    (b) Tick **three** things in the list below that lead to the formation of metamorphic rocks.

☐ pressure   ☐ magma   ☐ intrusion

☐ deposition   ☐ time   ☐ heat

    (c) Give **one** other example of a metamorphic rock.

....

Q2 Granite and basalt are examples of igneous rocks.

    (a) Basalt is an extrusive rock. Once it has formed, it immediately begins to get eroded (worn down) by rain and wind. Suggest why this is not true for granite.

....

....

    (b) The diagrams below show the structure of granite and basalt.

....

    (i) Write a name under each rock to show which is granite and which is basalt.

    (ii) Explain your answer to part (i).

....

....

Section 3 — The Earth and The Atmosphere

Q3 Steven found a fossil ammonite in a layer of sedimentary rock.
Some information about ammonites is shown on below.

Ammonite
- Sea creature with a hard shell.
- Descended from organisms that date back over 400 million years.
- First evolved 240 million years ago.
- Became extinct 65 million years ago.

(a) What is the **youngest** age that the sedimentary rock can be? Explain your answer.

....

....

....

(b) Complete this sentence by circling the correct word in the brackets.

The layer of rock with the fossil will be (**younger / older**)
than the layer directly below it.

(c) Explain how sedimentary rock is formed from sediment in the sea.

....

....

....

....

Challenge Yourself

Q4 **Slate** is a metamorphic rock which is often formed from **shale**, a sedimentary rock.
Fossils are found in shale, but they are very rarely found in slate. Suggest why.

....

....

....

Topic Review How do you think those questions went?
Have you got those learning objectives sussed?

Section 3 — The Earth and The Atmosphere

The Rock Cycle

Learning Objective
It might not seem like it, but <u>rocks</u> are constantly <u>changing</u> from one type to another. It takes a <u>really long time</u> though. At the end of this topic, you will...
- know the <u>rock cycle</u> and be able to describe what happens at each <u>step</u>.

The Rock Cycle Takes Millions of Years to Complete

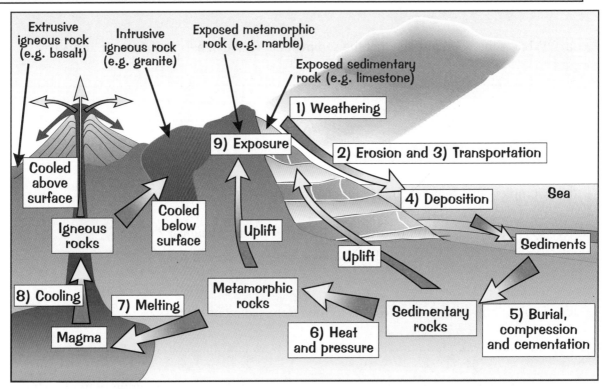

The rock cycle involves <u>changing</u> the three types of rock (<u>igneous</u>, <u>sedimentary</u> and <u>metamorphic</u>, see pages 80-81) from one to another. This happens in nine steps:

1) Weathering

<u>Breaking down</u> rocks into <u>smaller bits</u>. There are a few different ways this can happen, e.g:

<u>Onion skin weathering</u> — this happens when the Sun <u>warms</u> the <u>surface</u> of a rock by <u>day</u> and by <u>night</u> it <u>cools</u> down. This causes the surface to <u>expand</u> and <u>contract</u>, and eventually it <u>breaks away</u>, like <u>peeling an onion</u>.

<u>Freeze-thaw weathering</u> — when water <u>freezes</u>, it <u>expands</u>. If this happens in a <u>crack</u> in a rock it can make the crack <u>bigger</u>. After freezing and thawing many times, <u>bits break off</u>.

2) Erosion

1) This just means <u>wearing down</u> rocks until they <u>break up</u>.
2) Rocks can be eroded things like <u>rain</u>, <u>wind</u> or <u>waves</u>.
3) Erosion <u>always</u> involves <u>transportation</u> (see next page).

EXAMPLE:

Waves wear away at the cliff base.

Rocks above break off and collapse.

Rocks are carried away (see next page).

3) Transportation

1) The eroded bits of rock are <u>moved around</u> the world by <u>wind</u> and <u>water</u> (mostly).

2) <u>Sediments</u> are <u>transported</u> to <u>lakes</u> and <u>seas</u> by, e.g. <u>rivers</u>.

4) Deposition

1) Rivers transport <u>sediment</u> to lakes and seas where it <u>sinks</u> to the bottom.

2) This <u>laying down</u> of sediment is known as <u>deposition</u>.

5) Burial, Compression and Cementation

1) The deposition of new sediment <u>buries</u> the layers beneath, <u>squeezing</u> and <u>compressing</u> them.

2) <u>Water</u> gets squished out and the sediment particles are <u>cemented</u> together by other minerals (see page 81).

3) Eventually <u>SEDIMENTARY</u> rocks are formed.

6) Heat and Pressure

1) Further <u>squashing</u> and <u>heating</u> turn the rocks into <u>METAMORPHIC</u> rocks.

2) They don't melt — but the <u>minerals</u> the rocks are made up of may undergo <u>chemical reactions</u> to form <u>new minerals</u>.

7) Melting

1) <u>Intense heating</u> makes the rock partially <u>melt</u> — that changes it to <u>magma</u>.

2) Magma <u>flows</u> like a liquid because it is <u>partially molten</u>.

8) Cooling

When <u>magma</u> flows towards the surface of the Earth it <u>cools</u> to form <u>IGNEOUS rocks</u>.

9) Exposure

1) <u>New rocks</u> forming underground <u>push</u> the <u>old rocks</u> towards the surface — this is called <u>uplift</u>.

2) Rocks that end up <u>exposed</u> on the Earth's <u>surface</u> are subject to weathering and erosion — and the whole cycle <u>begins again</u>. Simple, huh.

3) The <u>amount</u> of rock on the surface is always <u>about the same</u>, even though it's <u>weathered</u> away.

Diagram labels: Sea, Sediment, Sedimentary rock, Metamorphic rock, Magma

Rip-roaringly Raucous Rock Cycle Questions:

Quick Fire Questions

Q1 Name two kinds of weathering.

Q2 What is the name of the process where bits of eroded rock are moved?

Q3 Which kind of rock is formed when deposited bits of rock are compressed?

Practice Questions

Q1 The diagram below shows the rock cycle.

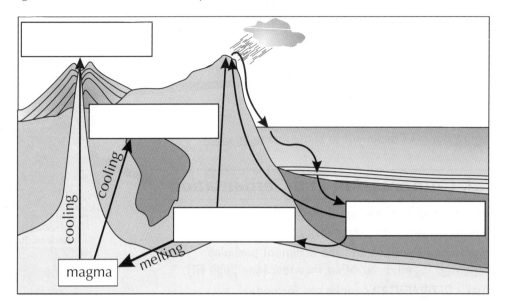

(a) How long does the rock cycle take to complete all its steps? Circle the correct answer below.

a few months   a few years   thousands of years   millions of years

(b) Use the names of the **three** different types of rock to
fill in the **four** labels on the diagram above.

(c) Write the **names** of the following processes next to the correct **arrow** on the diagram.

1 — Rock on the Earth's surface breaks down.

2 — Sediment is laid down.

3 — Rocks that have formed underground are revealed on the Earth's surface.

Q2 The different processes that rock goes through change it in different ways.

(a) What type of rock will metamorphic rock become after the following changes?

1. exposure
2. erosion
3. deposition
4. burial, compression and cementation

....

(b) What type of rock will sedimentary rock become after the following changes?

1. heating and compression
2. melting
3. cooling

....

Topic Review   Did you feel confident answering the questions?
Do you think you know the learning objective inside out?

Section 3 — The Earth and The Atmosphere

Recycling

We get everything we need to survive from the <u>Earth</u>. But these resources are <u>limited</u> — and that's where <u>recycling</u> comes in. After this section, you will...

- understand that we get a <u>limited supply</u> of <u>important resources</u> from the Earth
- be able to explain why <u>recycling</u> is important
- know that the <u>efficiency</u> of recycling can <u>vary</u>.

The Earth is the Source of All Our Resources

1) <u>Resources</u> are things we <u>use</u>. We get all our resources from the <u>Earth</u>, including:

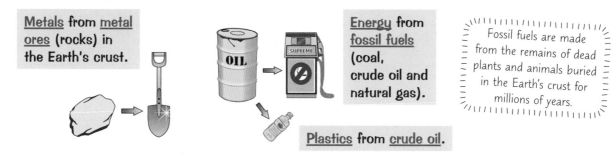

Metals from <u>metal ores</u> (rocks) in the Earth's crust.

Energy from <u>fossil fuels</u> (coal, crude oil and natural gas).

Fossil fuels are made from the remains of dead plants and animals buried in the Earth's crust for millions of years.

Plastics from <u>crude oil</u>.

2) But these resources are <u>limited</u>. Once we've <u>burnt</u> all the Earth's fossil fuels or <u>mined</u> all the metal ores, <u>that's it</u> — we <u>won't</u> be <u>getting any more</u> any time soon. And that's where <u>recycling</u> comes in.

There are Lots of Good Reasons for Recycling

Recycling means taking <u>old, unwanted products</u> and using the <u>materials</u> to make <u>new stuff</u>. Recycling is generally <u>better</u> than <u>making things from scratch</u> all the time because:

1) It uses <u>less</u> of the Earth's <u>limited resources</u> — things like crude oil and metal ores.
2) It uses <u>less energy</u> — which usually comes from burning fossil fuels.
3) Energy is expensive — so recycling tends to <u>save money</u> too.
4) It makes <u>less rubbish</u> — which would usually end up in <u>landfill sites</u> (<u>rubbish dumps</u>).

<u>Example — recycling aluminium cans:</u>

1) If aluminium <u>wasn't recycled</u>, more <u>aluminium ore</u> would have to be <u>mined</u>.
2) Mining costs <u>money</u> and uses loads of <u>energy</u>. It also makes a <u>mess</u> of the <u>landscape</u>.
3) The ore then needs to be <u>transported</u> and the aluminium <u>extracted</u> — which uses <u>more energy</u>.
4) It then <u>costs</u> to send the <u>used aluminium</u> to <u>landfill</u>.

It's a complex calculation, but for every <u>1 kg</u> of aluminium cans that are recycled, you <u>save</u>:

- <u>95%</u> of the <u>energy</u> needed to mine and extract 'fresh' aluminium,
- <u>4 kg</u> of aluminium ore,
- a <u>lot</u> of waste.

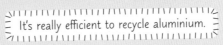

It's really efficient to recycle aluminium.

It's usually <u>more efficient</u> (in terms of energy and cost) to <u>recycle materials</u> rather than throw them away and produce new ones. But the efficiency <u>varies</u> depending on what it is you're recycling. E.g. you get an energy saving of <u>95%</u> by recycling <u>aluminium</u>, but less with <u>plastics</u> (<u>70%</u>) and <u>steel</u> (<u>60%</u>).

88

Reassuringly Restful Recycling Questions:

Quick Fire Questions

Q1 Name **two** things that humans use crude oil for.

Q2 Write a definition of recycling.

Practice Questions

Q1 Recycling materials usually uses less energy than making new ones.
Give **two** reasons why it's a good idea to use less energy.

Reason 1 — ....

....

Reason 2 — ....

....

Q2 **One** of the sentences below is incorrect. Circle it, and then rewrite it so that it is correct.

1. It's usually more efficient to recycle materials than throw them away and make new ones.
2. Recycling is efficient because it costs nothing.
3. Efficiency varies depending on what's being recycled.

....

....

Q3 Copper and tin are two metals. They're used to make the alloy, bronze.

(a) Copper and tin are both limited resources. What is a limited resource?

....

....

(b) It is possible to recycle both copper and tin.
Recycling tin is more efficient than recycling copper.
Suggest **two** reasons why some metals might be recycled more efficiently than others.

1 ....

....

2 ....

....

Topic Review Were you able to answer all the questions?
Do you think you understand all the learning objectives?

Section 3 — The Earth and The Atmosphere

The Carbon Cycle

Learning Objective
Just like rocks (pages 84-85), <u>carbon</u> is constantly <u>changing</u> from one form to another. Unlike rocks, <u>you're</u> a part of this cycle. When you've done this topic, you will...
- understand the <u>carbon cycle</u> and be able to <u>describe</u> each step.

<u>Carbon</u> is a <u>very important element</u> because it's part of all <u>living things</u>. As shown below, it's <u>constantly recycled</u> through the environment.

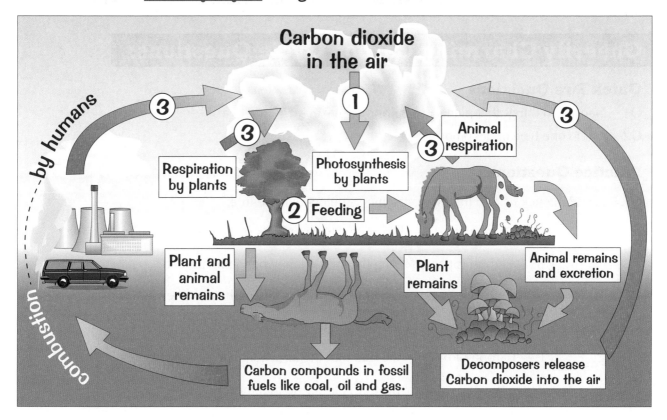

Learn these points:

1) Photosynthesis *Removes* Carbon Dioxide *from the Air*

1) <u>Green plants</u> and <u>algae (seaweeds)</u> all carry out a process called <u>photosynthesis</u>. It's how they make their <u>food</u>.

2) During photosynthesis, <u>plants</u> and <u>algae</u> take in <u>carbon dioxide</u> from the <u>air</u> and convert it into <u>glucose</u>.

Animals can't photosynthesise — only plants and algae (and some bacteria).

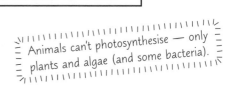
carbon dioxide + water $\xrightarrow{\text{sunlight}}$ glucose + oxygen

3) The plants and algae then use the <u>carbon</u> in the glucose to make <u>carbohydrates</u>, <u>fats</u> and <u>proteins</u>.

2) Carbon *is Passed Along the* Food Chain *When Animals* Feed

1) Some of the carbon in plants is <u>passed on</u> to <u>animals</u> when they <u>eat</u> the plants.

2) The animals then use the carbon to make <u>fats</u> and <u>proteins</u> of their own. The carbon moves along the <u>food chain</u> when the animals are eaten by other animals.

3) Respiration and Combustion Return Carbon Dioxide to the Air

1) All living organisms carry out a chemical reaction called <u>respiration</u>.
It's how they release <u>energy</u> from their food.

2) Respiration releases <u>carbon dioxide</u> as a <u>by-product</u>. So some carbon is
<u>returned</u> to the <u>air</u> as carbon dioxide when plants and animals <u>respire</u>.

3) When plants and animals <u>die</u>, <u>decomposers</u> (like bacteria and fungi) <u>feed</u> on them. Decomposers
also feed on <u>animal waste</u>. When the decomposers <u>respire</u>, carbon dioxide is returned to the air.

4) Some <u>dead plant and animal remains</u> get buried and eventually form <u>fossil fuels</u>.
When fossil fuels are <u>burnt</u> (<u>combustion</u>) this releases <u>carbon dioxide</u> back into the <u>air</u>.

Cheerily Charming Carbon Cycle Questions:

Quick Fire Questions

Q1 Name two things that plants use carbon to make.

Q2 Name one type of decomposer.

Practice Questions

Q1 (a) Put a tick next to the **three** statements below that are true.

☐ A — Photosynthesis is the process where plants make carbon dioxide.

☐ B — Carbon is passed along the food chain when animals feed.

☐ C — Only plants, animals and some bacteria can photosynthesise.

☐ D — Decomposers release carbon dioxide back into the air.

☐ E — Carbon dioxide is released into the air when living organisms respire.

(b) Rewrite the **two** false statements from part (a) so that they are correct.

1. ....

....

2. ....

....

Q2 Humans release carbon dioxide into the air by burning fossil fuels.

(a) Briefly explain why fossil fuels contain carbon.

....

....

(b) Give **one** other way in which humans produce carbon dioxide.

....

Topic Review Did you feel confident answering the questions?
Do you reckon you know the learning objective?

The Atmosphere and Climate

Humans are making some pretty <u>big changes</u> to the atmosphere — the layer of <u>gases</u> that surrounds the Earth. When you've finished this topic you should know...

- which <u>gases</u> make up the Earth's atmosphere
- how humans are <u>increasing</u> the amount of <u>carbon dioxide</u> in the atmosphere and what <u>effect</u> this is having on the Earth's <u>climate</u>.

The Earth's Atmosphere is Made Up of Different Gases

1) The <u>gases</u> that surround a planet make up that planet's <u>atmosphere</u>.

2) The <u>Earth's atmosphere</u> is around:

78% nitrogen (N_2)   21% oxygen (O_2)   0.04% carbon dioxide (CO_2)

It also contains <u>small amounts</u> of other gases, like <u>water vapour</u> and a few <u>noble gases</u> (see page 22). The amount of <u>water vapour</u> in the atmosphere is pretty <u>low</u>, but there's still <u>more</u> than <u>carbon dioxide</u>.

The Carbon Dioxide Level is Increasing...

The level of carbon dioxide in the Earth's <u>atmosphere</u> is rising. There are some natural causes, but it's mainly down to <u>human activities</u>:

1) <u>Burning fossil fuels</u> to power <u>cars</u>, and to make <u>electricity</u> in <u>power stations</u>, releases lots of carbon dioxide into the atmosphere.

2) <u>Deforestation</u> (chopping down trees) means <u>less carbon dioxide</u> is <u>removed</u> from the atmosphere by <u>photosynthesis</u>.

...Which is Affecting the Earth's Climate

1) Carbon dioxide is what's known as a <u>greenhouse gas</u>. This means it <u>traps heat</u> from the <u>Sun</u> in the <u>Earth's atmosphere</u>. This <u>stops</u> some heat from <u>being lost</u> into <u>space</u> and helps to keep the <u>Earth warm</u>.

This is a bit like what happens in a greenhouse. The Sun shines in, and the glass helps keep some of the heat in.

2) Over the past 100 years or so, the <u>temperature</u> of the <u>Earth</u> has <u>increased</u>. Most scientists think this is due to the <u>increasing</u> level of <u>carbon dioxide</u> (and a few <u>other greenhouse gases</u>) in the atmosphere.

3) This increase in the Earth's temperature is called <u>global warming</u>.

4) Global warming is a type of <u>climate change</u>. It seems to be having some <u>serious effects</u>, e.g.

- <u>Glaciers</u> and <u>ice sheets</u> covering Greenland and Antarctica are starting to <u>melt</u> faster, which could cause <u>sea levels</u> to <u>rise</u> and coastal areas to <u>flood</u>.
- <u>Rainfall patterns</u> are changing, which might make it <u>harder</u> for farmers to <u>grow crops</u>.

Actually All Right Atmosphere and Climate Questions:

Quick Fire Questions

Q1 Write a definition for a planet's atmosphere.

Q2 Name three substances that make up the Earth's atmosphere.

Q3 Which two human activities are causing the level of carbon dioxide in the atmosphere to increase?

Practice Questions

Q1 (a) What is global warming?

....

(b) Underline **two** problems below that could be caused by global warming.

Weathering of buildings   Rising sea levels

Failed crop harvests   Deadlier earthquakes   Increased CO_2 in the atmosphere

Challenge Yourself

Q2 The graph below shows how global temperatures have changed over the last 600 years. It was made by combining information from many scientists using sources such as historical records and direct measurements. Look at the graph and answer the questions which follow.

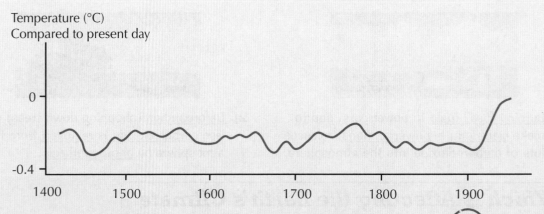

(a) What does the graph show about the changes in global temperature?

....

....

(b) What makes this data reliable?

....

(c) Suggest an explanation for the most recent change in global temperature.

....

Topic Review Are you out of breath after that mental workout? Are you confident on all the learning objectives?

Section 3 — The Earth and The Atmosphere

Index

A

accuracy 3, 4
acids 61, 62, 64, 65
  reactions with metals 70
  reactions with oxides 73
alkalis 61, 62, 64, 73
alloys 40
aluminium cans 87
atmosphere 91
atoms 19, 24, 49, 58, 59

B

balancing chemical equations 58
bar charts 5
basalt 80
boiling 16
burning 52, 90, 91

C

carbon
  in the reactivity series 67
  reduction reactions 68
carbon cycle 89, 90
carbon dioxide 89-91
catalysts 56
cementation 81, 85
ceramics 46
changing state 16, 17
chemical
  bonds 24, 49
  equations 58, 59
  formulae 25, 58, 59
  reactions 24, 49, 52, 55, 56
  symbols 19
chromatograms 33
chromatography 32, 33
climate change 91
combustion 52, 55, 90
composite materials 47
compounds 24
  naming 27
conclusions 6
concrete 47
condensing 16
conducting
  electricity 38, 42
  heat 38, 42
control variables 3
cooling curves 17
core (Earth) 78
crude oil 87
crust (Earth) 78

D

Dalton model 19
data 5, 6
decomposers 90
deforestation 91
density 7, 39, 43
dependent variables 3
deposition 85
diffusion 13
displacement reactions 75, 76
dissolving 29
distillation 34

E

earthquakes 78
Earth's
  atmosphere 91
  climate 91
  resources 87
  structure 78
electrolysis 68
electrons 38, 42
elements 19, 21, 22, 24
endothermic reactions 55
energy changes on changes of state 16, 17
equations 58
equipment 3
erosion 84
evaluations 6
evaporation 32
evidence 2, 3
exothermic reactions 55
exposure 85
extracting metals 68
extrusive igneous rock 80

F

fair tests 3
fibreglass 47
fieldwork 3
filtration 32
fossil fuels 87, 91
fossils 81
fractional distillation 34
freezing 16

G

gases 7, 9, 10
gas pressure 12
global warming 91
granite 80
graphite 42, 43
graphs 5
greenhouse gases 91
Group 0 elements 22
Group 1 elements 21, 22
Group 2 elements 22
Group 7 elements 21, 22
groups (periodic table) 21, 22

H

Haber process 56
hand warmers 55
hazards 4
heating curves 17
hydrocarbons 52
hydrogen 67, 70
hypotheses 2

I

igneous rocks 80, 85
independent variables 3
indicators 61
intrusive igneous rock 80
investigations 3, 4
iron extraction 68
iron sulfide 24

L

laboratories 3
limestone 81
limited resources 87
line graphs 5, 6
liquids 7, 9
litmus paper 61

M

magma 80, 85
magnetism 40
making salts 64, 65
mantle 78
marble 81
mass 49, 50
mean (average) 5
melting 16

Index